Men's Healing:
A TOOLBOX FOR LIFE

By
ALAN LYME, LCSW, CAP
DAVID J. POWELL, PhD
STEPHEN ANDREW, LCSW, LADC, CGP

Foreword by John Lee

HANLEY HOPE

PUBLISHING

© Hanley Center 2008
Copyright registration pending

ISBN 978-0-615-17269-9

FIELD REVIEWS

Finally, a book written for men, about men, and by men. Hell, if we can watch ads about treating erectile dysfunction during halftime, why can't we read a book about improving our inner lives? Be a man, pick it up. You'll be glad you did. *Scott D. Miller, Ph.D., Co-director, Institute for the Study of Therapeutic Change, co-author of The Heart and Soul of Change.*

Gender-specific treatment is long overdue! It's time to let go of the Super Hero and Marlboro Myths and honor men in their authenticity. The *Toolbox for Life* does that. With a wealth of experience these three colleagues have given the field an invaluable gift. *Claudia Black, Ph.D., author of It Will Never Happen to Me.*

At last!--a self-help book for *men*...written by men who really understand the challenges we men face in today's complex world. *Men's Healing* is an invaluable guide to the issues that we struggle with inside, but rarely talk about. But *Toolbox for Life* goes far beyond talk--it's filled with practical tips and exercises for a better inner and outer life. *Robert Gass, Ed.D., author of Chanting: Discovering Spirit*

Men's Healing is a book that touches and teaches at the same time. It is full of valuable insight about being male in contemporary America. As such, it raises many questions about men that are too seldom asked. More importantly, this book is a road map for men who want to successfully work through the challenges of our times. I highly recommend *Men's Healing* not only for all men, but also to those who want to help. I congratulate Alan Lyme, Dr. Powell, and Stephen Andrew on a nice piece of work! *Robert J. Ackerman, Ph.D., author of Silent Sons*

This book achieves two important functions. It will help both professional helpers and clients do their jobs. It is an excellent resource for professionals who are in need of information and a set of readily applicable tools. My male clients will find it helpful in their pursuit of personal growth. I will certainly use it extensively for my clients and will add it to the bibliotherapy list I give them. Thank you for this invaluable tool. *William L Mock, Ph.D., LISW, LICDC, SAP, Executive Director, Center for Interpersonal Development, Ohio*

I think you have filled a huge gap with this publication. I found it fascinating. I had just planned to read it for content, but as a man I found myself absorbed in the questions, the case studies, and the implications for use in treatment. It is a publication that treatment agencies will welcome. My hope is that it will also get into university curricula so that future counselors can become aware of the needs of men in treatment. *John Porter, M.S., Northwest Frontier ATTC*

Men's Healing was created and enriched by three distinct but deeply aligned sensibilities, each seasoned by experience and blessed with compassion. The book that has resulted from this synthesis is both rich and concise, both practical and inspirational. Those who read and apply it will be well informed and prepared to go forward with hope and purpose. *Archie Brodsky, B.A., Department of Psychiatry, Beth Israel Deaconess Medical Center, Harvard Medical School; co-author of Love and Addiction; The Truth About Addiction and Recovery.*

It seems that a book on *Men's Healing* would have a very specific and narrow audience. But it actually has lots of information, insights, and practical help for men, women, counselors, therapists, other helping professionals and programs. If you are a man and are considering this book, you are well on your way to getting the full benefit of the exploration and exercises inside these pages. If you are a woman, be prepared to understand and accept the men in your life much better. If you are a helping professional, there's a lot here that you were never taught and need to know. It certainly is a Toolbox for Life, whether used as a self-help/self-change process or in a treatment-assisted self-change program. *David Mee-Lee, M.D., Psychiatrist and Addiction Specialist, DML Training and Consulting, Davis, CA*

This is an excellent and informative book; a practical treatment manual that skillfully addresses men's issues and provides a superb set of skills, activities, and techniques specific to working with men. The authors provide us with a clear and thoughtful roadmap at a time when there is much confusion about what it means to be a man in the world today, and when gender roles are rapidly changing. It is wonderfully creative and offers a variety of methodologies that go beyond "talk therapy" and affectively-oriented interventions. The book also addresses deeper questions on "why" we live and succeeds in offering a new vision of what it means to be a man in society today. It is highly recommended reading for all clinicians working with men, and for men who are interested in the pursuit of self-discovery. *Patrick Reilly, Ph.D., Assistant Chief, Mental Health Services, Santa Rosa Veteran's Administration, Santa Rosa, CA, and Co-Chair, Men's Treatment Improvement Protocol, CSAT*

"Finally, a book written by men about helping men to heal. This is an excellent book. I heartily recommend it." *Christopher Kennedy Lawford author of Symptoms of Withdrawal*

ACKNOWLEDGMENTS

This manual began as a germ of an idea between Stephen Andrew and me. It was originally intended to be a small workbook to be used by the residents in the Center for Men's Recovery at Hanley Center in West Palm Beach, Florida.. With the addition of the prolific David Powell the work grew in size and scope and began to take on a life of its own. It became apparent that the manual might be of some use to a larger audience, with something for everyone. Deadlines came and went, marketing folks scratched their heads, and interested parties began to doubt that the work would ever be published. Through all the ups and downs, the work was buoyed by the solid unwavering support of Hanley Center's CEO, Terry Allen, and the unparalleled professionalism of our editor, Archie Brodsky.

On behalf of my co-authors, I'd like to thank Terry Allen for his belief in us, and Hanley Center for being the vessel that brought us together. I'd also like to thank John Lee for his beautiful foreword. He speaks of mentors, and I have been gifted with this golden opportunity to work with and be supported by mine.

In service,
Alan Lyme

TABLE OF CONTENTS

FOREWORD
by John Lee

The Sears Craftsman toolbox comes in a variety of colors and sizes, just like the men who use them. But the large red one on wheels with what seems like a million drawers is by far most men's favorite. It has room for dozens and dozens of tools the mechanic can pull out and use to make major and minor repairs and adjustments.

Shouldn't men in general and therapists in particular have a toolbox full of equally fine tools to help repair a man's life and his relationships? Wouldn't it be nice if you had an eighth-of-an-inch or half-inch wrench to tighten up or loosen up the nuts and bolts of recovery? Or perhaps you need a pair of needle-nose pliers to pull out all the things that got stuck inside you since early childhood, such as bad advice, barbed comments, and put-downs. And, of course, you'll need a vice grip to hold onto the things that were taken away prematurely, like vulnerability, trust, and feelings in general. Picture yourself pulling out a Phillips or flat-head screw driver that could be used to secure your relationships or to unscrew yourself from all the ways a man gets screwed by being seen as a success object or by screwing up his own life with drugs and alcohol. You have just such a toolbox right now in your hands.

Alright, perhaps I've carried the metaphor a little too far, so let's talk about mentors. Remember some years back the testosterone television sitcom *Home Improvement?* It centered around a fictitious show called *Tool Time* which was hosted by Tim "The Tool Man" Taylor (played by Tim Allen), a blue-collar worker from Michigan who was famous for grunting his affection for power tools and vintage cars and loving them only slightly less than his television wife and children. But the best part of the show was his relationship with his next-door neighbor and mentor, Wilson, who helped befuddled Tim with life's questions and conundrums. Now imagine that on the day every boy was born he was given not only a large shiny red emotional, spiritual, and psychological toolbox with everything in it he would need to work on his life, but also a wise, compassionate mentor. What would that boy's life look like, be like, and feel like? What if every time a monkey wrench was thrown into his relationships with his father, mother, lover, employer, or higher power he could walk into his back yard, poke his head over a fence, and ask his mentor for guidance? The book you have in your hand is like a mentor - filled with guidance and suggestions.

I've been working on my own "men's issues" and have counseled, coached, and facilitated men's groups, workshops, and conferences for nearly twenty-five years. I've read virtually every book written for and about men and have even written a few of my own. I've been taught by - and had the privilege to teach with - leaders in men's work; greats like Robert Bly, Dr. Robert Moore, Malidoma Some, Robert Johnson, and several others.

So when my friend Alan Lyme sent me *Men's Healing: A Toolbox For Life* and asked me to read it and write the foreword, I was a little reluctant to read yet another "men's book." Man, was I pleasantly surprised and delighted! I underlined all kinds of things I'd never heard said or never thought of before. The authors of *Men's Healing*-- Alan Lyme (LCSW, CAP), David J. Powell (PhD), and Stephen Andrew (LCSW, LADC, CGP), and are brilliant, powerful men. They not only have put their hearts, heads, and souls into this book, but also have included genuinely useful tools to help anyone who loves, lives with, or works with men.

The authors have achieved three very important things extremely well:

1. They have brought their collective knowledge, wisdom, and years of experience in working with men and put it in one *man*-ual.

2. They have successfully pulled together the best ideas, insights, information, and guidance from their own mentors and teachers into a single powerful book.

3. They have written it all down in a highly organized and very reader-friendly way-not always an easy thing to do.

To be a man in these ever-changing times is challenging to say the least. Speaking for myself, I need all the help I can get from wherever I can get it, to navigate my white-water ride through work, relationships, recovery, parenting, and friendship. I received some real guidance from reading this book and I know you will as well.

There is an old Arabic proverb that says, "A man sets out on a journey that takes him two hundred years to complete. If he had a good guide it would have only taken him two days." With this book, you have a good guide, a toolbox full of important information, and three mentors who are a step or two farther along on this journey into deep manhood and recovery. I hope you read it, do the very powerful exercises in it, ponder its wisdom, and pass it on.

INTRODUCTION

Real men don't ask for help! Most men are self-reliant, controlled, and seek medical or psychiatric assistance only when they are really sick. A man has to be half dead to see a doctor. Most men visit a doctor only upon the urging and cajoling of their partners. So many medical and psychiatric problems go unattended for years.

To date, little has been written concerning the issues, knowledge, and skills needed to work with men. It has been assumed that the literature in behavioral health treatment has traditionally addressed men's issues more than it has women's. However true this may be, it does not mean that men's issues have been adequately addressed. Even more importantly, the literature in the field concerning men tends to be quite broad, general, socio-cultural, and biochemical in nature. For example, the excellent Treatment Improvement Protocol for men, to be published by the Center for Substance Abuse Treatment, is a broad view of men's issues and substance abuse, with outstanding biological information but little concerning practical treatment issues when working with men.

What is needed is a practical manual that discusses the principles, methods, and specific skills needed for working with men--that is, the issues to be addressed and, most importantly, the therapeutic activities that can be utilized. The goal of this Manual is two-fold: to provide the behavioral health care field with a practical Manual for treating men, and to offer men a guide for self-discovery.

The hypothesis of this Manual is that men do better in treatment with gender-specific focus, where a variety of methodologies are employed, not just "talk-therapy" or "affectively-oriented" work. There are several qualities that most men have in common: a sense of competition and comparison; an action-oriented, problem-solving style when dealing with life issues; a clear sense of the "rules" in life (which are often learned through sports); and, currently, great confusion about what it means to be a man in a world where gender roles are rapidly changing.

We also propose that gender-related training is appropriate for all clinicians. Moreover, given the preponderance of female personnel in the helping professions, there is a special need to prepare female therapists to deal with male issues.

The core of this work germinated in the fertile soil of Hanley Center in West Palm Beach, Florida. Hanley Center offers gender-specific and age-appropriate treatment for those afflicted with alcohol or drug addiction as well as for the dually diagnosed. It was there that the authors came together and began to explore a joint writing venture. Alan Lyme, who had been engaged as the program director for the Center for Men's Recovery at Hanley Center, had consulted with Stephen Andrew of the Health and Education Training Institute of Portland, Maine, on both gender-specific treatment for men and the campus-wide training in Motivational Interviewing. Stephen, in turn, had introduced David Powell, president of the International Center for Health Concerns, to Hanley Center. David, author of *Playing Life's Second Half: A Man's Guide for Turning Success into Significance* (2003) and *Clinical Supervision in Alcohol and Drug Abuse Counseling* (2004), began a consulting relationship with Hanley Center on both working with men and clinical supervision.

This Manual is a collaboration among these three men who have a common vision. That vision includes freeing men from the bondage of their collective past and helping them to create a limitless future. We no longer have to pretend to be GI Joe, the Marlboro Man, or a Super-Hero. We do not have to perpetuate our fathers' addictions to work, alcohol, or emotional obscurity. We can feel, love, trust, and be vulnerable.

All of the material in this manual has been "field-tested" with the male clients at Hanley Center, and the results have been very encouraging.

The Manual begins with a review of uniquely male issues, such as the male socialization process, what it's like to be a man, and how men relate to emotions, sexuality, competition, and family. The Manual reviews key areas to address and treatment methods for working with men, including motivational interviewing skills and helpful educational modules for psycho-education. Practical techniques are presented for working with men, including exercises and activities, rites and rituals to perform, and men's rites of passage into a sober manhood.

The exercises are designed to be completed in a separate journal, whether by individuals using this Manual for self-discovery or by clients who are given the exercises by clinicians as therapeutic tools. Our hope is that clinicians will do the exercises themselves, when appropriate, before giving them to clients, so as to explore their own personal, emotional, and spiritual histories, the better to understand their clients' explorations. We took into consideration that some clinicians using this book to work with men will be women, and we hope the information contained herein will make their task a little easier.

The case studies are composites of a number of men with whom we have been blessed to work. They are included to illuminate the vast experiences, hopes, and aspirations of those who have had the courage to challenge their life-path. All names and identifying information have been changed to maintain anonymity and confidentiality.

PRIMER:
How to Use this Toolbox

This book is for men and women who wish to explore men's-specific issues. Although written about men, it is not exclusively for them. On the contrary, it is meant to be accessible for men and women together, for individuals seeking to better understand the lives of men.

This is a toolbox, a self-help book for men and those working with men. To take full advantage of the toolbox, we recommend that the reader take out of the box each chapter that is filled with specific tools for men to assist us on the journey. Tools are not helpful unless they are taken into the hand of a skilled person and fully utilized. Thus, this book is a guide that requires your active engagement. Simply reading through the issues may be interesting, but little will change for the reader unless you seriously consider and use the tools and recommended exercises. Change is not simply a mental activity; rather, it requires a shift in attitude and behavior as to how we work with men and how we as men walk on the journey of life.

Ultimately, this is a spiritual book, asking questions not only about how to live but also about why we live. It will encourage you to explore your spirit and the fundamental questions about what it means to be a man in today's ever-changing world. It is recommended that the reader use a journal to explore the exercises and activities individually and with others. Keeping a journal enables you to apply the perspectives in this book to your specific journey in life.

This book is a road map, a kit with tools. However, life is not a simple machine to be fixed and managed. Everyone is unique. The toolbox can provide you with a basic set of operating equipment. You need to adapt and apply the tools to your unique journey in life. The book will provide you with the following benefits:

1. A new vision of what it is like to be a man today.

2. The tools needed for dealing with the ever-changing issues we face.

3. A map to answer the basic questions of life, such as "What's it all about?" and "What gives me a sense of meaning and purpose?"

4. Tools to address areas such as substance abuse and addiction, dealing with our emotions, sexuality, work, money, fatherhood, and the barriers to being a wise, giving, fulfilled man.

5. Resources to work through key issues in life, including homework assignments; bibliotherapy; use of videos, poetry, and art; activities to pursue; and questions to answer.

6. An extensive bibliography related to men's issues.

As you read this book we encourage you to engage in the activities and answer the questions posed, seeking wisdom and not knowledge, insight and not data, and learning to live with life's unanswerable questions.

Section 1:

BEING A MAN

CHAPTER ONE:
An Environment of Risk.

The little things? The little moments? They aren't so little.
Jon Kabbat-Zinn

What does it mean to be a man in the 21st Century? To be a man in this millennium is to be in isolation. We are taught to be in competition with each other and to trust no one. We are expected to be sensitive to the needs of others. We are expected to provide for our families. How do we cope? Many cope by leading meaningless lives of desperation. Food, work, exercise, drugs, alcohol, sex, sports, religion, TELEVISION! We cope by avoiding the reality of our existence. Some men are fortunate enough to find support among their peers through social gatherings, church groups, or support groups. But for the majority, isolation is the key. When we isolate, we shelter ourselves from feeling. We cloak our emotions with superficiality. Smile for the camera called life. Research on men's issues yields the following data for the U.S. population:

- The majority of children abused, neglected, and murdered are boys (Kipnis, 1999).
- Most of the children in foster-care, shelters, and juvenile institutions are boys (Kipnis, 1999).
- 75% of student suspensions, expulsions, grade failures, special education referrals, school violence casualties, and all other assault victims are boys (Kipnis, 1999).
- 70% of suicides are boys/men (Center for Disease Control, 2006). 75% of teenage suicides are boys (Kindlom and Thompson, 1999).

- 80% of the homeless are boys/men (National Alliance to End Homelessness, 2006).
- 70% of drug addicts/alcoholics are men (Powell, 2003).
- 80% of homicide victims are men (U.S. Dept. of Justice, 2003).
- 93% of prison inmates are men (U.S. Dept. of Justice, 2003).
- 99% of executed prisoners are men (in the last decade, 700 men and 10 women) (U.S. Dept. of Justice, 2003).

Looking at these statistics led us to examine the underlying causes, as well as how men in the grip of addiction are affected by those causes. Within moments of being born, males are treated with less affection than females. Studies have shown that a newborn baby covered with a blue blanket will get touched less and will be spoken to in a firmer voice than the same baby in a pink blanket (Greenberg, 1979). Gender-stereotyping behavior on the part of adults--even those sensitive to gender issues--is endemic (Kivel, 1999). This sets the stage for induction into the "Boy Code," in which emotions need to be kept in check, violence is an acceptable response to emotional upset, self-esteem relies on power, and all "feminine" qualities must be rejected (Pollack, 1999). Boys may be starved for attention and put down as "sissies" if they cling and clamor for the closeness they need (Goldberg, 1976). Boys are traditionally taught to stuff all emotions through the often heard retort, "Big boys don't cry," or the more frightening threat, "I'll give you something to cry about." These early lessons teach them that it is not okay to emote, so all emotion is stifled (David and Brannon, 1976).

Men are conditioned to not feel or express pain, grief, or hurt. The feelings of love, joy, and excitement also can get numbed. Anger, though, seems to be permitted and encouraged. Anger is cultivated through team sports where the goal is to "beat" the opponent as severely as possible. Boys learn that men are expendable, a commodity readily traded for "God and country" (Keen, 1991). Many a five-year-old's life goal is to become a soldier, to fight. As boys grow into teens they can easily become engulfed in a "Culture of Cruelty" (Kindlom and Thompson, 1999), in which they are either victims, perpetrators, or witnesses of daily violence and humiliation. Boys are socialized to fear each other. This is the truest definition of male homophobia, the fear of men, which is rampant in our culture.

Boys are taught that their emotional needs cannot be met in their relationships with each other (Real, 1997), that to be too close to another boy may leave them labeled as "gay," and in that pubescent maelstrom, such a label is social suicide. This creates a vacuum in which boys need an emotional connection but may not have the social skills to obtain it in a healthy manner (Pollack, 1999). Parental guidance in this period is often fragmented at best. Fathers are often absent, either physically through divorce or work, or emotionally through their own shortcomings. Mothers can be extremely protective or overly dependent. William Pollack (1999) states that "at a very young age a boy may feel emotionally abandoned." Few boys survive childhood without some form of physical or emotional trauma, resulting either from the aggression of their peers or from the emotional separation from their parents (Pollack, 1999). Boys may learn to trust no one; instead, they "should" know how to take care of everything, how to fix everything.

It is not surprising, then, that so many men seek comfort with alcohol and drugs and that, for many, that initial comfort becomes a physical addiction. The void created by the trauma of boyhood can be filled, even if temporarily, by chemical enhancement. Pain can be numbed, shyness can be masked, and anxiety can be ameliorated. The need for connection without intimacy can be met. But what happens when the substances stop working, when the consequences of using them become unbearable? The unthinkable act of asking for help can only be overshadowed by the inability to receive it when it is offered (Goldberg, 1976).

Challenging belief systems: what is it like to be male?

This is the dilemma: How can we teach men, who are socialized to be incapable of sustaining trust, that their only hope of relief is to trust and to allow themselves to become vulnerable with their peers? Since this was anathema to their survival, the transition could be difficult. In essence, when men enter treatment, we are asking them to challenge the very core beliefs they have lived by. In our work we ask the question, "What is it like to be male?" The answers invariably include the following: lonely; isolative; armor-plated; judged; seen as a threat to women, children, and each other; aggressive; expected to perform, provide, and protect. When compared to what we ask of men in treatment (to be vulnerable; share emotions; take risks; cooperate; believe; accept others' ideas), it is easy to see how men could initially perceive treatment as threatening, if not impossible.

Our first goal in treating men at the Hanley Center, therefore, was to create an environment in which men could feel safe enough to allow themselves to open up to each other. Our belief was that by creating a safe space, emotional movement would occur. This environment included having an all-male staff with which to interact, thereby breaking the cycle of relying on women to meet emotional needs (Goldberg, 1976). It was important to examine the socialization process that was common to the western male. Five areas were outlined and educational modules were created to help the men in residential treatment understand the how and why of their behavior. These areas are outlined here and explored in detail in some of the chapters that follow:

1. Being a Man: We take a good look at our societal standards of "real" masculinity. Dovetailing with the work of Paul Kivel (1992) we address the boxed-in stereotype that drives men's beliefs about themselves. We examine the roles that men are expected to fill and the anxiety attached to those roles. We talk about the limitations of forcing ourselves to fit inside the box, and the incredible social price paid by those who dare to challenge the boundaries.

2. Men and their family of origin: This component examines childhood messages and paints a picture of the dynamics that have led to a life of addiction and/or isolation. We look at the role of fathers and explore how men can begin to parent themselves if necessary. Art and psychodrama are explored as vehicles with which to tap into the unconscious, where many of our early traumas are stored.

3. Men and Emotions: The emotion most commonly identified by the men in our groups is anger. Anger is accepted and often expected from men in our society, yet when inappropriately expressed it is destructive of the fabric of our culture. This educational component explores the distinction between the emotion of anger and the action of aggression, which is often blurred by early modeling. We take a look at rage, which is what many men think of when they talk about anger. We also address issues of power and control as they relate to interpersonal relationships. Normalizing anger, untangling it from rage, recognizing its emotional cousins fear and shame, and opening a dialogue help to begin the process of learning to express anger in a healthy manner

4. Men and Sexuality: The connection between drug and alcohol dependence and promiscuity is apparent (Schneider, 1992), but beyond that there is an underlying cultural belief that men "should" know about sex and that a "real man" can always please his partner (Keen, 1991). This module addresses how looking at sexual values and mores in a group setting can remove the bravado factor and allow men to take an honest look at their beliefs. We address the issues of sexuality, sexual dysfunction, and sex addiction.

5. The Male Spiritual Journey: We examine how to engage men in safe, non-threatening, and non-judgmental dialogue concerning spiritual matters. As men discover that spirituality is all about connecting to life, whereas active addiction is all about disconnecting from life, the importance of spiritual development to recovery becomes more and more clear. Spiritual development requires that a man develop an ability to trust and eventually to rely on elements that are outside of himself. In stark contrast, men are taught from a very young age to be independent and self-sufficient. Although this is often an indirect correlation, men tend to conclude that to rely on anyone or anything else is a form of weakness which will shortly be exploited (Goldberg, 1976). Overcoming this dysfunctional early learning requires an environment where vulnerability and trust are redefined as *strengths* rather than *weaknesses* and as acts of *courage* rather than of *cowardice*. As they experience this environment, men become more open to allowing themselves to clear the cobwebs from their spirits and begin to experience life and peace.

These components help form a framework for men to begin to identify with each other and help open the door to the possibility of community, which is often preconceived as unattainable or unnecessary. They also serve as the backbone for our work. We hope that this book will be useful both for the individual in self-discovery and for the clinician as a therapeutic tool that may be used in group work and one-on-one counseling in both residential and outpatient settings.

CHAPTER TWO:
Growing Up Male

If you treat an individual as he is,
he will stay as he is,
but if you treat him as if he were what he ought to be
and could be,
he will become what he ought to be and could be.
Goethe, 1749-1842

How can men be emotionally oppressed in our culture? We have economic power and are bigger than women and children, right? But how we perceive male hurt makes a profound contribution to all male addictions, compulsions, and obsessions, whether sex addiction, alcoholism, or other drug addiction. It affects men of any race or color. Boys and teenagers are dying from the male socialization process. There must be something systemic in our culture, something our disease concept doesn't yet address that pushes men into the disease of addiction. What environmental factor in our socialization process creates the discomfort in men that leads them to alcohol, nicotine, and other drug addiction? One part of the answer is the socialization process for men that starts when we are just boys.

When we're born, there's no difference between men and women in our ability to emote, our ability to think and figure things out, our ability to connect and be intimate, and our ability to be close to other human beings. These abilities are universal when we're born. We all have the ability to be spontaneous, the ability to love and to be loved, and we all have a strong yearning for power and control over our own destinies. There is no difference between boy babies and girl babies. None of these abilities and desires is gender-specific.

Hold that thought-no difference. No difference. Then something happens to us. Bit by bit, the male socialization process implants beliefs about maleness in us. Shame-based beliefs that begin to chip away at our self-esteem, our self-worth. Beliefs that chip away at our ability to be our natural selves.

What are these beliefs we're socialized to accept that tear us from our natural selves? How about the belief that:

- Men aren't supposed to feel.
- "Good" men are strong, athletic, and physical.
- Men are expendable.
- Men aren't good at intimacy.
- Men and boys are basically violent.
- Men must be the only providers, protectors, and/or fixers.

These beliefs, born in our culture and transmitted through our media, literature, and the collusion of our society, tear us away from our true core selves. And there are powerful consequences of this training by our culture. These beliefs devalue men's lives.

Men are taught to believe that there are many things more important than themselves, like fighting for their country or protecting their families, or that they are only as valuable as they are good at providing for and protecting others.

Men are placed in competition with each other. They perceive situations as only win/lose whether they are or not. Men constantly compare themselves to each other, as if all resources are limited and every situation is a zero-sum game, whether it is or not. This way of thinking turns all other men into potential enemies, not sources of support in our lives or, more importantly, life sources such as our own male relatives.

And when men lose, they feel shame. These "particles" of shame collect like dust on the soul, dimming our zest for life. A man begins to separate himself internally between his inner "good guy" and his inner "bad guy." The culture rewards this competitive process through popular media and in life. The rewards are money and the resulting status.

Men are rewarded in this subtle and intense process of competition where nothing is more important than winning. But this kind of winning also implies losing. And men win and lose in two ways. We're rewarded if we win over somebody else, competitive sports being a primary example. But we lose out on non-competitive activities for boys where everyone can win. This sticks out all the more sharply if you just try to imagine what our culture would look like if we intentionally encouraged collaboration, respect, empathy, and teamwork as the priorities of a young man's life.

Men can permit themselves to entertain only the emotions that are consistent with the attitude to win, succeed, and achieve. How else can they accomplish those feats? Once you begin to demand success and a "winner attitude," men must use aggression.

Our whole culture thrives on cultivating aggression in boys. Boys start being exposed to cruelty among one another starting at age 8 or 9, the same age that boys start paying more attention to their peers than their families. This boyhood aggression lasts until they reach about 15 years of age. Until then, it's just "play," "boys being boys." While they're still minors, it's as if our society gives young men permission to be aggressive. And what comes with this permission? First, poor impulse control in dealing with anger; second, depression, from holding in anger in every situation in which they fear aggression or receive it.

These are the two main behaviors men develop to manage our emotions-aggression and depression. Fueling each other in a feedback loop, the vicious cycle of aggression and depression results in the cultural perception that men are insensitive, unemotional, violent, sex-driven, and basically inhumane.

These cultural messages are brought home to us when we are still very small boys, unable to protect ourselves from them. In other words, we grew up watching our fathers and mothers teach us about being men. And we saw and heard mixed messages: on the one hand, men should be strong and reliable; on the other hand, men are naturally insensitive, violent, compulsive, and non-nurturing caregivers. At some point after you were born and declared a boy, you started being touched less and less in a nurturing way, and more and more being touched "hard" with a slap, a pinch, or a poke. You were being toughened up.

This uneven approach to the genders creates a deep unsatisfied hunger for attachment and affection, a pattern developed over the course of our formative years. Is it any surprise that many men become addicted to sex, the means of attachment that involves physical touch--in other words, nurturing? Data suggests that men are three times more likely than women to seek help for sexual addiction (Schneider and Weiss, 2001). A sexual addiction rate of that magnitude occurring so disproportionately in one gender-our gender-has deep roots in the systemic failure to meet boys' very basic need for attachment. We want to be touched. We yearn for emotional attachment. By the time we are adults, there's a deficit that feels as if it could never be filled.

So let's go back to that fact that there is no fundamental difference between men and women at birth-both need to love and be loved, to feel capable and powerful, and to be connected to others. The social script that casts men as too aggressive, too sexual, unable to show any emotion other than through anger, and incapable by nature of being caregivers to their children produces a constant stream of blows to our self-esteem. Instead of toughening us up, it softens us up for anything that will ease the pain. It sets men up for addiction.

Why addiction? Because we can numb ourselves and our pain with addictive substances: alcohol, cigarettes, caffeine, and other drugs. Is it any wonder that we develop the disease of addiction? Men develop the disease of alcoholism and other drug addictions at a rate of three men to one woman (Lemle and Mishkind, 1989). After lifetimes of these contradictory messages about ourselves (don't feel except anger, don't trust other boys, don't get too close to other boys), after years of not having had our basic attachment needs met and being encouraged to buy into the attitude that girls are objects for our pleasure and/or emotional nurturance, we live in contradiction with our true selves, in a world of hurt.

We all have some level of underlying depression as a result of working so hard to do it right, to be perceived as a "good" man. And since we have no internal resources to repair the hurt, we find something external, something "manly" and acceptable to repair or medicate our emotional pain.

Case study: Ken

Ken is a 54-year-old in a 15-year relationship with his partner. Over the last five years, Ken's partner has taken primary custody of her two grandchildren, eight and nine years old. Child welfare officials have expressed concern that Ken's drinking is negatively impacting the children and have mandated Ken to addiction counseling if he wants to be involved in their lives.

Ken is an amazingly caring man who finds himself at a time in his life when he is very ambivalent about having authorities inform, advise, help, or support him. Ken isn't one who can easily accept help or support because it re-stimulates feelings of shame that he cannot live as quietly and independently as he would like. He does not like being the focus of others' attention. Truth be known, his natural instinct is to fade back and avoid notice. That way he feels he can manage things his way, without others' advice or help. He has issues with people telling him what to do.

Ken is fairly rigid about the "right" way to do things and will go pretty far, even to the point of conflict, to rationalize doing things his way. His history of accepting help has been spotty. He comes to one or two therapy sessions and then decides to go it alone. Ken is clearly ambivalent about other people, especially those in authority. He struggles to know what to do about his adopted grandchildren's "high needs." He is sensitive about being told the "right" thing to do for the children, especially because he believes that he is able to prescribe age-appropriate parental interventions for different situations. His strong concern for the kids has created a purpose in his life.

This purpose has given him the strength to step away from substances-to take the opportunity to stop using, even though he has found that very hard to do. Ken has stopped using all illicit drugs, such as marijuana and cocaine. He loves dancing, going out, being social; movement is especially important to him. Ken is extremely intelligent, compassionate, and thoughtful and has a nice way of thinking about other people. He has an interest in Buddhism, spirituality, and other healing issues.

Ken's impulsiveness is triggered by his distaste for authority and being controlled. This has caused him a great deal of anxiety as well some medical problems he now struggles with. He's ambivalent about quitting drinking because he doesn't believe that this particular behavior has impacted his children's development. He is angered by any kind of authoritative intervention, which he sees as unwarranted interference. He mostly feels hopeless about this attitude. Because Ken also doesn't trust peers, he is unwilling to participate in a group setting on a regular basis. This will make it extremely difficult for Ken to stay sober and clean.

Exercise:

Take a few minutes to find a journal and pen, and put on some relaxing music near a comfortable seat in a quiet place where you will not be interrupted. Sit down and write each of the following prompts at the top of its own page. Then, under each prompt, identify and list some of the deep hurts you received in your past from the male socializing process.

1. What were some of your father's teachings or messages to you?

2. How did he teach you to "be a man"?

3. Are you ashamed of something you did to another boy when you were a teenager?

Now return to the page with your first prompt. Take a deep breath and exhale slowly several times. Reread the prompt and your answer. Feel your courage and your strength to hear your own truth.

Take another deep breath and let yourself feel what was good and what hurt about that moment in your male socialization process.

Take another deep breath and think about how that moment connects to your present life and who you are now, and how it may have contributed to your addictions or compulsions.

You can use the rest of the page to write down the connections your reflection uncovered or any other thoughts that occur to you.

Repeat this process for the other two prompts.

Closure: Read out: I promise I will be proud to be a man who will seek the closeness in brotherhood of every man, of every age, race, nation, and class. I will permit no slander or disrespect or blaming of any man for the hurts that have been placed upon him. I will seek to restore safety to all men to release the cruel hurts. I will fight to end and eliminate the burden of men's over-responsibility and over-fatigue. I will cherish my birthright as a man and I will cherish being a good, intelligent, courageous, powerful male human. I promise.

CHAPTER THREE
Substances of Use

To many, total abstinence is easier than perfect moderation.
- Saint Augustine of Hippo (354-430)
Doctor of the church, Bishop of Hippo, b. Algeria

Why do men drink? What is it that drives a man to seek out an altered state of mind? For many men there is a correlation between their initial introduction to alcohol and their initiation into manhood. Drinking takes practice! The bitter taste of most beer and liquor is not an immediate favorite for most neophyte drinkers. But it is not the taste that hooks, it is the effect. So what really happens when we drink? There are many physiological changes that occur in the body when you add alcohol, but what of the emotional and social effects?

Many men describe alcohol as a social lubricant. The initial freedom from the bondage of self-doubt and uncertainty: uncertainty of how to act, how to fit in, how to "be a man." Time and again we hear men say that they "needed" a drink or two to quell the inner voices that prevented them from socializing sober. The problem for many men is that the line between "socially comfortable" and blackout is frequently, unintentionally, crossed.

For many men, the consumption of alcohol is accepted as a rite of passage. Reports of college fraternity pledges dying of alcohol poisoning are all too frequent. Some of our most hallowed institutions of learning are more famous for their parties than for their faculties. For some, these years of alcohol abuse are left behind upon graduation, and a life of moderate social drinking is adopted. For others, the abuse of their teens becomes the addiction that shapes the rest of their lives.

Some men learn to drink like their fathers. For others, the behavior of their fathers promotes a life of complete abstinence.

Marijuana, cocaine, LSD, ecstasy, methamphetamine, heroin, anxiolitics, and a variety of other drugs are frequently part of a man's journey. Whether upper or downer, each drug has its own unique pathway to "somewhere else." Somewhere else, anywhere else, is often preferable for a man who may be riddled with pain, shame, fear, and self-doubt. There may not be a definitive moment when a man moves from abuse to addiction. For some, a genetic predisposition has left them wide open to dependence. For others, years of abuse have left them physically unable to stop using. Either way, the outcome was similar: strained relationships, physical and emotional bankruptcy, missed opportunities.

The following is a case study of one man's journey from substance abuse to addiction to recovery.

Case Study: Chris's Story

Chris had his first blackout at twelve years old. He had been sneaking drinks from his parents' liquor bar since he was five. He and his younger sister had long been in the habit of finishing up the many half-empty glasses on the mornings after one of their parents' numerous parties.

But this was different. He was at a party thrown by some older kids, and the alcohol was freely available. Chris had limited social skills. He was afraid of what others thought of him. To say that his family was dysfunctional would have been an understatement. His father was alcoholic, his mother a rageaholic.

He had learned how to manipulate his parents, how to lie, how to steal, and how to be violent. He had not learned how to be comfortable in his own skin. So here he was, his first major social event during puberty, and he was completely lost.

The last thing he remembered about the evening was throwing a drink over one of his friends who was kissing a girl that he liked but didn't know how to approach. Blackout. Throw up. Fall down.

This became a regular event for Chris. Drink. Blackout. Throw up. Fall down.

At school, violence was a daily occurrence. Being punched in the arm, thrown into a headlock, kicked to the ground was routine. He was a less than average student, smaller than most of the other boys, and hyper-aware that he didn't fit in. Gravitating towards the drinkers, the smokers, the vandals, he began spending less and less time at home. He managed to avoid being arrested on luck alone.

He became obsessed with pornography at thirteen years old and longed for a physical connection with a female. Having narrowly escaped several homosexual advances from older men, he had learned to be homophobic. He feared all men.

At fourteen he had intercourse for the first time. It was a horrible, humiliating, embarrassing experience for him. The alcohol he had consumed in order to raise his courage lowered his ability to perform. The fifteen-year-old girl, who was more experienced than Chris, grew impatient and verbally abusive toward him.

His alcohol consumption increased. The more he drank, the less he felt, the more advances he made toward people who meant less and less to him.

He began smoking pot at fifteen. He also had his first real sexual relationship with a 23-year-old neighbor. She would tap on his window when she was drunk and climb into his room. She taught him that sex could be pleasurable. She taught him about a woman's body. He felt good in her arms. Then she was gone. He wanted desperately to have a loving relationship. At fifteen years old he knew that he wanted to be loved, that he had never been loved. He had felt something like it in this woman's arms, and began to equate love with sex. He never considered that what had transpired was abuse. At sixteen he again met a girl of his own age whom he really liked. When she became willing to be sexual he once again became impotent. She laughed. He cried with embarrassment and anger.

He vowed to never go through that again. He began to drink more frequently. He lost interest in pursuing sex and became vigilant in his pursuit of getting wasted. His impotence lasted for a year. He could feel it whenever he became close to a woman he liked. After a year he discovered that he felt aroused around women he didn't particularly like. He discovered that he could be sexual as long as there was no emotional involvement. Closeness without intimacy. His childhood had taught him that intimacy was dangerous, that it was painful. And now as he approached his manhood he was incapable of intimacy. Now he sought physical gratification without risking intimacy.

He had dropped out of school before his sixteenth birthday, left home, and lived for a short while with a variety of friends and relatives. He left each place after his drinking and drugging became intolerable to his host. Even the most loving friend or relative could only take so much. Chris threw up frequently and was sometimes incontinent while sleeping. He began to explore other drugs: methamphetamine, LSD, and cocaine. He continued to smoke cigarettes and pot and drink on a daily basis.

Chris became dependent on women to rescue him. Never comfortable with more than superficial male relationships, he honed his skills to charm and conquer older women who could offer him food, shelter, and sex.

After his father died of his alcoholism, Chris spun out of control. He was a social chameleon, adapting to the wants and needs of whomever he felt he needed for survival. One night in a bar he met the woman who was to become his first wife. She was fifteen years older, divorced with four grown children, and starved for attention. Chris performed his way into marriage. She took care of him, cleaned up after him, drove him home when he was too wasted to move, and didn't ask too many questions when he didn't come home. He treated her like a doormat. She loved him. Each was as debilitated as the other, and they needed each other. They spent six tumultuous years together, through countless affairs on his part. He continued to seek validation sexually every opportunity he had.

Finally he could pretend no longer. During a drunken blackout he drove his car off a bridge. It's tough to deny that there is a problem when your car is submerged and you are suddenly cold, wet, and afraid. He was arrested and charged.

Then came his first commitment to change, to stop drinking, to stop cheating, to change his life. He realized almost immediately that he couldn't stop. He called the AA hotline and was told that the nearest meeting was in a church. He couldn't go to a church. He didn't believe in God. He hated religion. He began to think of suicide. It wasn't a new thought, just stronger than ever before. He wrote his wife a note, apologizing for how he had treated her, and headed to his favorite spot on the beach. On the way he picked up a bottle of vodka and refilled a prescription for Valium. On the beach he began drinking and popping the pills. Slowly and deliberately. Eventually he passed out, not expecting ever to wake again. Five hours later, he woke up with the worst headache and the worst sunburn that he had ever had. Even in suicide, he was a failure.

It was at that moment that Chris decided to seek professional help. He wound up in a drug and alcohol treatment center for 28 days. The center was co-ed. Chris was given a female counselor and placed in group therapy with three women and five other men. He had a hard time staying focused, finding himself more interested in the females in the room, posturing and placating them, than in trying to explain his feelings to the group. He wasn't even sure what he felt. The only feelings he was ever certain of were anger and fear. He was told he was in denial. He was told he was going to die unless he surrendered to his disease.

Each day away from alcohol and drugs helped him feel better physically. He was taken to 12 Step meetings but felt no connection. He told no one of his sexual escapades, of his countless affairs. He developed a crush on his therapist and worked hard to stay in her good graces. After he completed treatment he had a brief affair with a woman he met in the program. She got pregnant and wanted to start a life with him. He was still married and his life was becoming more unmanageable in sobriety than it had been while drinking. The girlfriend moved away and later had a child he has never seen. His wife took him back… again.

For the next year he worked hard at staying sober and being faithful. He had made no real connection to anyone in treatment, had not been able to stay focused enough to benefit from his sparse attendance at 12 Step meetings, and became sexually involved with the first "recovering" woman who showed him attention. Sober and miserable, he was still behaving like the lonely teenager that he had been. When confronted by his now desperate wife, he became angry and full of rage. After she filed for divorce, he felt as though he had nowhere left to go. So he went back to the one friend he knew he could count on, alcohol.

Despite asking for help, Chris had not been able to connect with the help offered. His drinking and drug use continued for two more years until he was hospitalized following an overdose of Valium. When it was suggested that he enter treatment again he was reluctant. He felt it would be a waste of time and money. But the hospital social worker told him that she knew a place that was different, where he would really be able to find the help he wanted.

The second treatment center was different. Chris was in an all-male setting, with all-male counselors. He was scared at first, as he had never been comfortable with other men, but he slowly came to see that he was not so different from his peers. He was challenged to take a good look at his life, at where he had been and where he was going. He was encouraged by his counselor to stay open to all possibilities. A spiritual counselor helped him work through his fear and anger toward God. The men played sports and games together. They laughed at and with each other and cried with each other. He began to experience a strange emotion…hope.

With the help of his peers Chris began to feel that it might be possible for him to get and stay sober. He completed treatment, continued in aftercare, remained connected to his peers, and stayed sober. He put aside his bias and attended 12 Step meetings, men's meetings. He obtained a sponsor and began to work through the steps.

Different treatment, different results.

What made the difference? What was it about the second treatment program that was successful? Was it simply that Chris was finally "ready to get well," that he had "hit his bottom," that he no longer was "in denial," was "resistant no more" (the "excuses" clinicians often give when a man drops out of treatment), or was there something about the quality of this program that worked?

As Chris's story unfolds, it seems apparent that the frequency, variety, and amounts of substances he used had a direct correlation to the frustration and emotional pain he experienced. Much of that frustration and pain is common to many men in our society. His story may be very different from your own, or from that of men you know, but each of us has a history that continues to unfold and affect our every interaction.

Knowing why a man became dependent is not as critical as his willingness to recover from that dependency, but it certainly can help to take a good look at some of the significant events over the lifespan of each man and to look for correlations in the types and amounts of substances used and the consequences incurred.

Exercise: Substance use inventory

In your journal, answer the following questions:

1. When was the first time you got drunk or high? How old were you and who were you with? What were the circumstances?

2. What feelings were affected by your substance use? How were you physically affected?

3. Write a time line of any changes in your choices of substances. How old were you? What did you use or stop using? What was happening in your life?

4. How were your expectations of yourself affected by your use?

5. What are the major consequences of your use?
> Physically
> Emotionally
> Relationally
> Financially
> Spiritually

CHAPTER FOUR
Men and Addiction - The Facts

All philosophy lies in two words, sustain and abstain.
- Epictetus (50-138)
Greek philosopher

Here are the facts about men and substance use and abuse:

1. SAMHSA studies (1996 and 2000) have found that the vast majority of American men over 12 years of age (82.6%) had used alcohol at least once in their lifetime. The data indicate that 9% of men reported heavy alcohol use (five or more drinks at one time in the previous month), compared to 2% of women. Approximately 34% of the sample reported using illicit drugs. Studies also indicate that drug use patterns vary significantly by racial and ethnic groupings.

2. Men are more than twice as likely to develop substance use disorders as women. Men begin using substances earlier than women (Brady and Randall, 1999) and have more opportunity to try drugs (van Etten, 1999). Men become intoxicated twice as often as women and are 3-4 times more likely to experience problem drinking and alcoholism (Lemle and Mishkind, 1989). These patterns cross all demographic lines of race, income, education, marital status, and geographic location.

3. Men suffer far more adverse consequences of substance abuse than women (Wilsnack et al., 2000). Clearly, the social construction of masculinity plays a significant role in these statistics (Brooks, 2001).

4. Men's attitudes toward alcohol and drugs tend to be generally less negative than women's attitudes. The use of substances is not viewed as a problem for men but rather as a rite of passage, a sign of true manliness. By contrast, substance use is more likely to be viewed as something for women to avoid due to increased sexual vulnerability. Moreover, such behavior is viewed as incompatible with female roles, including family and relationship expectations (Wilsnack et al., 2000).

5. Co-occurring psychiatric disorders occur commonly among men. In one study, Swartz and Lurigo (1999) found that 55% of the men identified as having a substance abuse problem also experienced mental health problems. Men often suffer from depression in conjunction with a substance abuse problem. On the other hand, men are not as likely as women to express their feelings of guilt, sadness, or worthlessness (all signs of depression) and may engage in reckless behavior as a way to deal with their depression. Men are also at greater risk of depression when they have experienced a trauma such as combat, an accident, or physical violence.

6. Men are also at greater risk for co-occurring medical problems, such as disorders of the liver, pancreas, and the neurological and gastrointestinal systems. Heavy alcohol use correlates with greater risk of prostate cancer and lower amounts of testosterone (Emanuele and Emanuele, 1998; Dennis and Hayes, 2001). Men who abuse alcohol are more likely to engage in unprotected sex and are at greater risk of contracting HIV, hepatitis, and other STDs.

7. Violence is closely associated with substance use and abuse among men. The relationship between early childhood sexual trauma and substance abuse in men has been well documented (Liebschutz et al., 2002; Ouimette et al., 2000). Substance using and abusing men also show high rates of violence.

8. Men who use and abuse substances also tend to have higher rates of

problems related to fatherhood and families. They are twice as likely not to pay child support as those without alcohol and drug problems (Garfinkel et al., 1998). Substance abuse and violence may also be a factor in separating men from their families. The results of this alienation are dramatic: when men are not in relationships or do not have children they are less likely to complete treatment (Rabinowitz and Marjefsky, 1998).

Biological Aspects of Men and Alcohol/Drugs

Distinct differences in drinking and drug-taking behavior exist between men and women across cultures and ethnic groups, although the neurobiological action of psychoactive drugs is essentially the same for men and women (Hanson, 2002).

First, in terms of genetic factors and alcoholism, although men and women differ on many drinking-related dimensions, data are contradictory regarding gender and genetic risk for alcoholism. Jang, Livesley, and Vernon (1997) reported significant genetic effects on alcohol and drug problems only in men, whereas environmental factors have a greater effect on women. These data suggest that "there appears to be converging evidence that increased male risk is attributable to both inherited predisposition and environmental risk factor-but risk for females is only attributable to environmental factors (Jang et al., 1997, p. 1271).

Contrasting findings are reported by Heath (1995), who found no significant gender differences with respect to genetic contribution to alcoholism risk. On the other hand, Walters (2002) suggests that the inheritability of a predisposition to alcoholism is stronger in males. In Asian populations, Tu and Israel (1995) conclude that "The female gender per se constitutes a major protective factor against alcohol consumption and alcohol abuse." (Tu and Israel, 1995, p. 63). When taking all of the research into account, it appears that the risk of inheriting alcoholism is higher for men than women. On the other hand, environmental factors appear to be more strongly involved in alcoholism among women (Schuckit et al., 1998).

Alcohol is known to affect the endocrine system, which does its work by means of various hormones that regulate bodily functions such as growth and reproduction. The part of the endocrine system concerned with male reproduction is called the hypothalamic-pituitary-gonadal (HPG) axis. The male reproductive system is governed by the interaction of the hypothalamus, a region of the brain, the pituitary gland, located at the base of the brain, and the gonads (testes). Alcohol, which affects all three parts of the HGP axis, is linked to low testosterone and altered levels of additional reproductive hormones (Emanuele and Emanuele, 2001).

Additionally, as the HPG axis is affected, increased use of alcohol has a detrimental effect on the production of testosterone and is associated with increased levels of prolactin and estrogen in men. The impact of these changes is a condition called gynecomastia, which is the enlargement of breast tissue, atrophy of the testicles, loss of body and facial hair, and a general feminization of muscle tone.

Other biological correlatives to alcohol and drug abuse and dependence include:

- Changes to the immune system
- Chronic brain syndrome
- Wernicke-Korsakoff Syndrome (understood to be caused mainly by the malnutrition often associated with alcoholism. People are at risk for W-K when they regularly drink instead of eating). Korsakoff's
- Psychosis is a particular manifestation or exacerbation of W-K Syndrome.
- Alcoholic pellagra
- Diabetes, gout, and respiratory disorders
- Gastrointestinal disorders, such as esophageal, stomach, and intestinal diseases
- Alcoholic pancreatitis, endocrine, and liver disorders
- Cardiovascular disorders and cancer

There is also a relationship between substance use in men and smoking and other disorders, such as sexually transmitted diseases, AIDS/HIV (NIAAA, 1992, 2000). In addition to alcohol-related disorders, other drugs of abuse can result in significant biological concerns.

Although these effects are fairly consistent for both men and women, the fact that many men rarely see a physician or have routine medical check-ups or care means that men entering an addiction treatment program may have several of these disorders, but have never been screened for them. Hence, a thorough physical examination is an essential part of addiction treatment for men.

CHAPTER FIVE
Men and Emotions

When we walk to the edge of all the light we have
and take the step into the darkness of the unknown,
we must believe one of two things will happen -
there will be something solid for us to stand on,
or we will be taught to fly.
Claire Morris: A Manual for Life

I was much further out than you thought. And not waving but drowning.
- Stevie Smith (1902-1971)
Not Waving but Drowning

"What is it about men and their emotions?" women ask. "Why can't they express their feelings?"

For most men, freely expressing emotions was not encouraged as we grew up, with the exception of anger. We're out of touch with many other emotions: sadness, grief, loss, and even love. If you are a man, did you ever sit in the den watching an emotional movie and surreptitiously wipe the tear in the corner of the eye away for fear of being seen as "emotional"? Thus, it is important for men to face a variety of feelings they may have been stuffing down through the years. This is best done "sideways," not directly. Instead of asking men to "talk about your feelings," often it is more effective to address emotions through activities and rituals.

When we think about our emotions, other than anger, we rarely fully express the range of our feelings. Yet our emotions run the gamut from happiness and joy to depression and despair. It is important for men to explore questions such as:

1. What makes you happy? What gives you a sense of energy, joy, peace?
2. What brings you to life? What gives you meaning and passion?
3. What emotions inside of you are waiting to come out? To happen?
4. What emotions do you experience in your family, friendships, children, religious group, social life?

Facing our fears is also an essential step for men. Although we're told as adult men to "suck it up, face your fears, never let them see you sweat," as children we learn how to distinguish between fears of real things and imagined fears. By the same token, we need to face our real and imagined fears about life. "Will we have enough? What if I lose my job? How can I successfully support my family? What if something happens to one of the children?" Today, in a world filled with terrorist threats, random violence in our towns and cities, and natural disasters, we need to address questions such as :

1. What do we fear about our job, our family, our life style, our world? With whom can we share our fears?
2. What skills do we have and use to deal with these fears?
3. What are our views about health, about death? What does death mean to us? What emotions come to us when we have to face the deaths of family, friends, and even ourselves?
4. How do we live in the in-between times of life? What emotions do we have when we do not know where we are or in what direction we're going?

Anger is the one "legitimate" emotion men can express, although it is often inappropriately identified and expressed as rage. John Lee, in *The Missing Peace* (2006), speaks to the manifestation of that rage and offers strategies for the appropriate expression of anger. However, men and the people in their lives should not lose sight of what often lies beneath the anger: namely, loss and sadness. Many men have a well of loss, grief, and sadness in their lives they have never expressed. To get to these emotions we may have to "come in the back door" through activities, rituals, films, and experiential therapies.

Exercise I: The Grieving Cup

The Grieving Cup is a valuable ritual that is quite effective with men. Good rituals need to fulfill two purposes: they must be authentic and identify something that is undeniable and true in men's lives, and they must be dramatic to break through men's denial and reluctance to address emotions. This activity can be done individually or in a group with a leader. The following is written as a group exercise. At the end of the case study it is presented as if an individual were doing the ritual himself.

If the exercise is being done in a group, the leader starts off with a small cup. It is best if the cup is made of clay and has an earthy feel to it, such as a Native American cup. Next, the leader introduces the ritual and gives those present the opportunity to participate or opt out, if they wish.

The group leader explains the ritual by saying something like, "Today, men, we will have an opportunity to remember an individual in our lives for whom we are grieving. This is a Native American pot that I purchased in Arizona. I will pass the pot around the circle and you are to silently whisper the name of an individual for whom you are grieving. It might be the name of your deceased father, a friend that you've recently lost, a lost relationship, a loved one, or perhaps your addiction. When you breathe the name of that person into the pot, hold that person close to your heart and pass the pot to the next man in the circle. After all have breathed a name into the pot, I will take the pot back and bless the pot."

The following is a hypothetical interchange that might occur in a group, should it be done with a leader. As the cup is passed around the circle of men, each member silently speaks the name of an individual into the cup.

"I breathe the name of my father, whom I have not seen in years."

"My wife, who recently died."

"My son, whom I have not seen in a decade because of my addiction."

"My teenage son, who died when he was 10 years old."

"My best friend, who is ill with prostate cancer."

"My boss, who hates me because of my drinking on the job."

"My daughter, from whom I am estranged due to my drinking."

"I grieve for my early years that my addiction took from me. I never really got to have a youth time, as my dad left my mom when I was a teen and I had to grow up quickly, be the man of the house, and tend after my mother. So I escaped into the bottle."

"My son, who will not speak to me any more."

"Myself and all I wanted to be in life but failed to achieve."

The leader then holds the cup in two hands and raises the cup over his head. He says something like, "Having spoken the name of someone for whom you're grieving their loss, I now dedicate these names. We hold them sacred. They have brought us great pain in our lives. We need to be released from that pain. We are now free from that grieving. Ashes to ashes, dust to dust. I now return these names back to the ground from which they came." The leader then smashes pot on the floor. Pottery chards splinter all over. The room is hushed. He says, "Men, we have returned these names to the earth. You are free. Who would like to begin to express what is happening for him at this moment?"

The following is an exchange which might occur.

George: "I feel a great sense of release. As if I don't have to hold on to that grief and pain any longer. After 20 years of being angry at my father for dying when I was 10 years old, I can now let him go."

Michael: "Wow, I did not expect you to do that. I am surprised, although I have a real sense of peace for the first time in my life. No longer do I need to hate my boss for what he did to me. It's gone."

John: "I am really pissed off at you. How dare you! I breathed the name of my departed son into that pot. And you broke that pot. And then, to make matters worse, you stepped on the chards. That really makes me angry."

Dan: "When my father died, I was just a boy, a teenager. I never really got to know him. For all of my life I have held anger toward him for abandoning my sisters and me. Now, for the first time in my life I feel a sense of release. I can let him go."

Mark: "I am shocked at the way you threw the pot on the floor, in total disregard for my feelings. I guess anger is a common emotion for me, but that's not what I am feeling toward you (the leader) right now. I am feeling sad that this is what life comes to, a few spoken words, said in silence, and a broken life scattered on the floor. Is this what life is about?"

Craig: "I feel relief. My wife died recently, and I have held back the tears for too long. Is it OK to cry for her now?"

David: "Because of my addiction, my boss has come to resent me, my lousy lifestyle, my poor performance. I am at times a superstar at work, at times a terrible employee. I guess that's what I grieve the most. Although I breathed the name of my boss into the pot, I guess I really breathed my own loss of myself, my potential, and my possibilities into the pot. I grieve for myself."

Lucas: "I have lived with so much pain in my life, physical pain from athletic injuries in high school and college. I use drugs and alcohol to relieve that pain. I never knew what they were doing to my body. I have never transformed my pain, only transmitted it onto others and my body. When you broke the pot, I felt pain relief, like that pain was being transformed for the first time in my life. Thank you."

Henry: "I am angry that you dashed so many feelings onto the floor. You seemed to have no respect for the value of the lives in the pot. Why did you do that?"

James: "Thanks for that sudden release. I needed something like that to break through my emotions, which I have kept bottled up in my own pot of self-pity. The pot is a beautiful image for me of my life, all self-contained, pretty on the outside, so many emotions on the inside; they remain there, inaudible, unobserved. When you broke the pot you broke through that wall of containment."

Leader: "Let's talk about our anger. At what other things, people, or events are we angry? Who else in the group is angry now, at something or someone?"

John: "I am angry at you for dashing the pot. I guess I am also angry at the world. It just seems so unjust, unfair. Why am I alcoholic? Why did my dad beat my mother? Why did he have to die at such an young age? I am angry at all of these things. I'm angry at my dad for dying, for abandoning me when I needed him, especially now that I am trying for the first time in my life to be clean and sober. He never really took good care of himself. He drank too much, too. He often beat my mother and me, but I still loved him. And just when I was trying to get my act together, he dies on me. That really pisses me off."

Leader: "How, John, have you dealt with that anger and pain of loss?"

John: "I took my early anger and rage out on myself, through my drinking and drugging. But I don't want to do that any more."

Leader: "If we don't transform our pain we transmit it. What would it mean to you, John, to transform your pain? Who else in the group has pain they'd like to transform?"

Lucas: "As I said earlier, I have a lot of pain I've never transformed. I take it out on my wife, the dog, my kids, myself. My addictions have numbed me to the pain. What does it mean to transform one's pain?"

Mark: "I need to transform my anger, too. I'm still feeling angry about what you did with the pot. How can I deal with that feeling? Tell me more about transforming pain. I don't know how to let go of the feelings I have for people that have let me down in life. It seems as if someone is always disappointing me."

Leader: "Tell us more about your disappointments in life."

In our hypothetical example, Mark might go into an extended statement about his disappointments-lost jobs, lost friends, lost loved ones, lost children, lost parents. The leader opens up the discussion to other group members to talk about disappointment and pain in their lives. The leader and the group discuss how they can transform their anger through letting go of their pain, surrendering to it, turning it over to their Higher Power. He says, "Who else has these feelings? Who else has had pain in their lives? What have you done to transform your pain?"

Craig: "I have had so many physical ailments over the years. First my back went out, then I had high blood pressure, bad knees from sports injuries, and now I find I am diagnosed with prostate cancer. Like my body is falling apart. And my alcohol and drug use made it easier to deal with my physical pain. I don't know what I am going to do without alcohol and painkillers. I want to transform my pain but I don't know how."

Matthew: "What has helped me is the First Step of AA, to be able to let go of my pain and to turn it over to my Higher Power. Once I saw I was powerless over my pain, that no matter what I did, I could not prevent problems from occurring. But I could at least not let it greatly affect me. That's how I've transformed my pain, and boy, I have had a lot of pain in my life."

Dan: "How does one let go when you've been so hurt? I need to learn because the problems I've had have just eaten away at me."

Leader: "Who can help Dan with his question? Perhaps we can go back to how we felt with the exercise earlier, recalling the feelings we had then?"

Often, at this point, group members discuss the pain they have felt in their lives. Many men speak of how they transmit their pain onto themselves through their drug and alcohol abuse. This opens the group to a depth of emotions previously unattainable without some form of ritual that breaks through defenses and denial. The group discussion about this ritual goes on for several sessions as deep emotions are expressed.

At the end of the session, group members are invited to pick up a piece of shard and keep it as a token of the release of their pain. The leader asks the members to keep the shard and bring it back to the next group meeting to discuss what that shard has meant to them throughout the week.

This ritual illustrates the form of dramatic, authentic activities that can be used in groups with men. By this physical portrayal, emotions are quickly brought to the surface in a way that might not otherwise happen with men in therapy. Participants are given an opportunity to journal their reactions to the ritual.

As indicated above, individuals can engage in a similar activity by themselves. Obviously, the emotions brought to the surface through the smashing of the pot may be intense, so it is best to have a friend or spiritual guide nearby to discuss these emotions.

The exercise can include the following questions to be completed in your journal:

1. What emotions are you holding which are eating away at you, which you need to release? Whom are you grieving?

2. If what we fail to grieve becomes a grievance, to whom and in what way do you need to let go of long-held resentments, grieving, feelings? Whatever remains unspoken and unaddressed becomes unspeakable. The 12 Steps address this process of making amends and resolving unresolved issues.

3. How long have you held these grievances? How have these emotions affected your life?

4. What do you need to do to let go of these feelings? What's standing in the way of your expressing these feelings?

Exercise II: Saying Goodbye

As an alternative to the Grieving Cup ritual, you might consider writing a goodbye letter to people in your life whose loss you still grieve. Begin by sitting quietly and relaxing your body, perhaps trying a form of meditation through breath and progressive body relaxation. The following is a form of relaxation exercise you might start off with.

Place your feet on the floor, put your hands wherever they are most comfortable, and close your eyes if you can. Take in a deep breath, as far as you can...exhale. Again breathe deeply, filling your lungs with cool air...exhale, breathing out all that moist stale air. Once more, inhale deeply...hold it.... Then exhale. Continue breathing deeply. Bring your focus to your feet, from the tips of your toes to your ankles, and as you focus on your feet, they become more relaxed. Now place your focus on your legs, from the ankles to the knees. As you focus on your legs from the ankles to the knees they become more relaxed. Continue in the same manner up to the top of your head.

Continue with deep breathing, focusing on "peace" on the inhale and "surrender" on the exhale.

Now to begin the process of saying goodbye to people in your life that you've been holding on to far too long, visualize yourself standing in a thicket of woods. Look around. This may be a place that is familiar to you. Perhaps you were here as a boy or as a man. You can see the sunrays shine through the thick canopy of trees. You can feel the warm sunlight on your face. You can smell the earth, the decomposing vegetation. You can hear the buzzing of insects and whistling of birds in the trees. As you look around you notice that you are standing on a path that stretches out before you. You begin to walk along the path, and as you do you can hear the twigs and leaves crunching underfoot.

In the distance you can hear running water, and the ground begins to rise and then falls into a stream. You cross over the stream and up the bank on the other side. You continue on the path and the woods get thicker. Suddenly you see a clearing up ahead. It is a large clearing, about the size of a football field. In the middle of the clearing you can see a group of people standing in a circle, with their backs toward you. As you get closer you begin to recognize some of the faces. These are the people who love or loved you. Visualize who these people might be. Their faces are saddened, and there are tears in their eyes. What if they were gathered here because this was your funeral? What if you were never to see these people again in this life? What do you want to say to these people? What do you want them to know about your struggle, about your love for them, about your sorrow?

Write a letter to these people in your journal. Read to yourself what you have written to them. Is this enough?

Exercise III: Emotional line-up

Answer the following questions to yourself, perhaps writing your answers in your journal:

1. What emotions do you most commonly feel--for example, anger, resentment, fear, anxiety, happiness? How have the emotions you feel changed in the course of your life?

2. What or whom do you need to grieve? Where do these feelings come from?

3. Write a timeline of events in your life that have brought you joy, happiness, peace, satisfaction, etc.

4. Write a timeline of events in your life that have brought you sadness, anxiety, depression, anger, etc.

5. Compare these two timelines in terms of their impact on your life and what you need to do to focus more on the positive and less on the negative events in your life.

6. How have these events shaped your current emotional state?

7. What are the consequences of these events for how you deal with your emotions now?

8. How have these events affected you physically, emotionally, socially, and spiritually?

Emotions. That's a tough one for us, as men. As we have emphasized, often the only legitimate emotion we see expressed by our fathers or other men in our lives is anger, and that is most frequently released as rage. But it is important for us to not use our anger to protect what really might be lurking beneath the surface. Often, it is a feeling of deep sadness and loss, from sources long since buried in our lives. These exercises are simple ways for us to get in touch with the sea of emotions that rides below the surfaces of our lives.

Men and Depression

Depression can strike anyone regardless of age, ethnicity, background, socioeconomic status, or gender. However, research has shown that depression is about twice as common in women than in men. In the U.S., researchers estimate that 12% of women (more than 12 million women) and 7% of men (more than 6 million men) are affected by depression in any given one-year period. (For detailed information on the symptoms, types of depression, co-occurrence of depression and other illnesses, and causes and etiology of depression, the reader is referred to *Men and Depression,* NIHM, NIH Publication # 03-4972).

Men experience depression differently from women and have different ways of coping with the symptoms. Men may be more willing to acknowledge fatigue, irritability, loss of interest in work or hobbies, and sleep disturbances than feelings of sadness, worthlessness, and excessive guilt (Pollack, 1998).

For many men, substance use and abuse can mask depression, making it harder to recognize depression as a separate illness that needs treatment. Instead of acknowledging their feelings, asking for help, or seeking appropriate treatment, men may turn to substances when they are depressed, or they may become frustrated, discouraged, angry, irritable, and sometimes violently abusive. Some men deal with depression by throwing themselves compulsively into their work, attempting to hide their depression from themselves, family, and friends. Other men respond to depression by engaging in reckless behavior, taking risks, and putting themselves and others in harm's way (Cochran & Rabinowitz, 2000).

Four times as many men as women die by suicide in the U.S., even though women make more suicide attempts. In addition to the fact that the methods men use to attempt suicide are generally more lethal than those used by women, there may be other factors that protect women against death by suicide. Because men are less likely to seek treatment for their depression, they are also more likely to die from suicide than to be diagnosed or treated for the depression that underlies the suicidal ideation.

Elderly men are particularly susceptible to depression and substance abuse. If men have been the primary wage earners for their families and have identified heavily with their jobs, they may feel stress upon retirement-loss of an important role, loss of self-esteem-that can lead to depression. Similarly, the loss of friends and family and the onset of other health problems as a result of aging can trigger depression for men. Health care professionals can miss depressive symptoms in older men, who are often reluctant to discuss their feelings of hopelessness, sadness, loss of interest in normally pleasurable activities, or extremely prolonged grief after a loss and who may complain primarily of physical symptoms.

Suicide is a special concern for aging men. There is a common perception that suicide rates are highest among the young. However, it is elderly men, particularly older white men, who have the highest suicide rates. Over 70% of older suicide victims have been to their primary care physician within the month of their death, many with a depressive illness that has gone undetected.

Only in the past two decades has depression in young men been taken seriously. Before puberty, boys and girls are equally likely to develop depressive disorders. After age 14, however, females are twice as likely as males to suffer from depression or dysthymia. The risk of developing bipolar disorders remains approximately equal for males and females throughout adolescence and adulthood (Worthman, 1993).

Suicide rates for teenage boys are alarmingly high. In 2000, suicide was the third leading cause of death among young males age 10-24. Among adolescents who develop major depressive disorders, as many as 7% will die by suicide in their young adult years (Shaffer et al., 1999).

The good news is that depression in men is treatable, with a good prognosis, through the proper use of medications, psychotherapies, electroconvulsive therapy, and/or herbal therapy. Family and friends can assist. Care givers need to be particularly sensitive to the possibility of depression in men, especially in adolescents and older male adults. For more information, the reader is referred to http://www.mentalhealth.samhs.gov.

CHAPTER SIX
Family of Origin

Could I climb the highest place in Athens, I would lift my voice and proclaim, "Fellow citizens, why do you turn and scrape every stone to gather wealth and take so little care of your children to whom one day you must relinquish it all?"
- Socrates (469-399 BC)
Greek philosopher in Athens who devised the Socratic method
of inquiry and instruction

Where did you come from? What was it like growing up in your family? Quite frequently we hear men share that they came from a "good" home, that they had "great" parents, and yet when we explore further there is often a tale of terror behind the lace curtains. Apparently "good" and "great" are relative terms.

A man's experience as a child can color his whole life. The role models who set the stage carry a heavy yet often invisible responsibility. How a father treats a mother, how he treats his children, his work ethic, his religious beliefs, his eating habits, his drinking habits (or addictions), his political beliefs, his bigotry or egalitarianism--these all have a direct impact on his offspring.

Many factors affect a boy's upbringing. For approximately half of the men born in the past thirty years, divorce colored their early home life. Given that the majority of children in a divorce are placed in the care of their mothers, many men were raised primarily by their mothers, with weekend or absent dads. Re-marriage, step-parents, and step-siblings often created confusion, emotional withdrawal, and a general lack of stability. For a boy to carve a sense of what it is to be a man from such a splintered family tree was a difficult task indeed.

Some were fortunate enough to have male role models from outside of their nuclear family who helped them with their transformation. Others struggled through adolescence, reaching adulthood with no blueprint of what being a healthy man looked and felt like.

Even when mom and dad were together, often there was little connection with dad, who was either absent through work or emotionally absent through his own lack of a healthy parental role model. Many men, therefore, were essentially raised by their mothers. Mom was looked upon to meet all emotional needs.

At their annual Men's Gathering workshop in Mentone, Alabama (2005), John Lee and Robert Bly (www.mentonemen.com) both spoke of the need to heal the relationship with mother. They posed the question: "Whose son are you? Your mother's? Your father's?"

They hypothesized that if the childhood relationship with and emotional dependence on mother are not consciously released, then a man can have no successful primary love relationship. There is no emotional room for healthy love if a man's head is still focused on pleasing Mom. This is manifest in the epidemic of men who are unable to engage in a healthy intimate relationship. The sky is full of aging Peter Pans, circling bewildered and embittered women who are left wondering where all the "good" men went.

John Lee uses an exercise designed to help men release the baggage of their relationships with mom (PEER Training, Inc.). In this exercise he has a man sit facing him, holding his hands. He then encourages the man to close his eyes and say the following:

"Mom, I need to let you go."

"Why do you need to let me go?"

"I need to let you go because…."

"What else?"

The pattern is repeated until the exhausted, emotionally spent man has nothing left to release, and ends with him saying, "Goodbye, Mom."

If mom or dad was an alcoholic, or if the family home was chaotic, certain roles may have been assumed by each family member. These roles were captured by Sharon Wegscheider-Cruse (1990), who skillfully detailed how they help family members both to grow up successfully and to appear as healthy as anyone else. Each role has its purpose, its strengths, and its needs for transformation. The roles are:

1. Family Hero: He is the one who can see and hear more of what is really happening in the family and begins to feel responsible for the family pain. The role of Hero is to provide a sense of "self-worth" for the family.

Family Hero strengths: hard workers who know how to get what they want.

Family Hero needs:
>   a. To learn to ask for and take what he needs.
>   b. To learn to accept failure.
>   c. To relax.
>   d. To focus on self and stop "fixing" family.

2. Scapegoat: He is the one who is in the public eye. Having learned that he must perform, he gets much of his needed attention in destructive ways. The role of the Scapegoat is to provide a distraction from the family.

Scapegoat strengths: Can see reality, has good insight, sensitive and courageous.

Scapegoat needs:
>   a. To get through the anger to the hurt.
>   b. To learn to negotiate instead of rebel.

3. Lost Child: He is the quiet one who never causes trouble. He feels hopeless and unimportant. He is often confused and fearful. He has learned to not make connections within the family. The role of the Lost Child is to offer relief. This is the one child the family doesn't worry about.

Lost Child strengths: He is patient, creative, and independent.

The Lost Child needs:
>   a. To reach out.

      b. To deal with loneliness.

      c. To face pain.

      d. To make new close relationships.

4. Mascot: He is tense, anxious, and often over-reactive. He defuses explosive situations by focusing attention on himself. He becomes a silly adult,whose relationships are often shallow and flighty. The role of the Mascot is to provide fun and humor.

Mascot strengths: He is humorous and knows how to enjoy himself.

The Mascot needs:

      a. To take responsibility.

      b. To risk being serious.

      c. To be assertive.

Because of the self-delusion and the compulsive nature of these behavior patterns, family members take them into every other relationship. Nonetheless, roles that were rigidly held in childhood can be changed in later years, depending on the needs of a given situation.

Exercise I: Family roles

Do you recognize yourself in any of the roles listed above? Answer the following questions:

    1. What was your role in your family?

    2. How has the role you played as a child affected you as an adult?

    3. How are these roles being played out with your own children?

Lucia Cappachione (1999), in *Recovery of Your Inner Child,* hypothesizes that in each of us lies a vulnerable child. Her work promotes reconnection with that child by providing a blueprint for examining childhood wounds. Her use of non-dominant handwriting and drawing, although not suggested without clinical supervision, has a therapeutic effect of breaking through the intellectual wall we often build to protect that inner child.

Exercise II: The Family Genogram

A genogram is like a family GPS. Take a blank sheet of paper and map out your family. Use circles to denote the females and squares to denote the males. Draw lines between each to represent the nature of the relationship. If the relationship is positive, use a solid line. If it is negative, use a broken or dashed line. Create as large a genogram as you wish, branching out into uncles, aunts, and cousins if you have them. The object is for you to gain a realistic perspective on your family relationships and how your own relationship patterns were developed.

Answer the following questions:

1. Who were you closest to in your family?
2. Who did you fear the most?
3. What did you learn about relationships from your family?
4. With whom do you share behavioral traits?

Exercise III: The Family Home

Turn to a blank page in your journal and draw a picture of the house you grew up in. There may have been several houses, but draw the first one that comes to your mind. You may draw a floor plan if it works better for you, but the idea is to jog your memory and return to that place. What happened in that house? Draw yourself and your family members: mom, dad, brothers, sisters. Put yourself in any room or any part of the yard that holds energy for you. As you sense yourself there, answer the following questions:

1. Why did you place yourself where you did?
2. What happened in this place? Was it painful or was it joyful?
3. How did whatever happened here affect your life?
4. Who protected you at that time?
5. Who protects you now?

Patterns of behavior that served to protect us as children often present as liabilities in our adult lives. The very same coping mechanisms that kept us from the wrath of our perpetrators can keep us from developing healthy primary relationships. Perhaps you learned as a child that it was dangerous to tell the truth. Maybe there were times when telling the truth led to physical or emotional abuse. The boy who gets spanked for spilling his milk will soon learn to say anything to avoid that spanking: "The dog did it" or "My baby sister did it".... Deflect, obfuscate, deny.

Case Study: The Liar's Path

Tom told lies. He lied when it would have been just as easy to tell the truth. Lying was a survival skill for Tom. When he was a boy he had been punished for telling the truth. Once. He never forgot it.

There were occasions as a child when he would brag about his family, making up grand stories of exotic vacations, swimming pools, and boats. Other times he would pretend that he had no family, telling people that he was an orphan or an only child. As an adult, he exaggerated his abilities and skills in the work environment, often finding himself faced with the truth only after he had created a mess.

It was in primary relationships that Tom's lying became most pervasive. Sometimes overt, often covert, always present. He had, from an early age, been taught that if he was to be happy, then he had better find someone to take care of him. He also learned from his father that it was okay and even expected that a man would cheat on his wife. This set the stage for a life of doomed relationships, always ending in bitterness and tears. Tom, always seeking the "woman to take care of him," would frequently overlap his affairs, beginning a new one before ending the last. He blew through two marriages and countless shorter-term relationships because of his reckless attitude toward them.

When he finally found his "dream-mate," Tom also found that the patterns of a lifetime were not necessarily put aside at will. Despite his best intentions, and often, seemingly, against his own will, he continued to lie. In seemingly innocuous conversation, when there was no possible gain from not telling the truth, he would lie. He often believed his own stories to the point of not knowing his own reality. Countless attempts to be "completely honest" with his mate led to frustration. It seemed that there was no solution. He felt as though he kept repeating the same mistake; only the details changed. It took several years of effort and a patient, tenacious partner to finally begin to break the pattern.

Exercise IV:

In your journal answer the following:

1. Where have you been dishonest in your life, if anywhere?
2. How has your dishonesty served you? How has your honesty served you?
3. How has your dishonesty harmed your relationships?

Practice honesty as you move through the day. Where does this seem more difficult? What feelings surface if and when dishonesty enters your relationships?

CHAPTER SEVEN
Sexuality

If it weren't for pickpockets, I'd have no sex life at all.
- Rodney Dangerfield (1921-2004)

The fountains mingle with the river
And the rivers with the Ocean,
The winds of Heaven mix for ever
With a sweet emotion;
Nothing in the world is single;
All things by a law divine
In one spirit meet and mingle.
Why not I with thine?

Love's Philosophy
Percy Bysshe Shelley, (1792-1822)

An open discussion of sexuality is not on the top of most men's "to-do" list. There is an underlying cultural belief that men "should" know about sex and that a "real man" can always please his partner (Keen, 1991). It is a rare man who will openly discuss his fears and uncertainties about his sex life. Looking at sexual values and mores in a group setting often removes the bravado factor and allows men to take an honest look at their beliefs. Issues of sexuality, sexual dysfunction, and sex addiction, although often taboo subjects, are of primary importance to any man struggling to sort out the truth from the messy messages of youth.

For many men, their earliest sexual experiences were fraught with performance anxiety and were far from the utopian pinnacles of pleasure that they had expected. Peer pressure, the mandate to succeed, the expectation that they "should " know what to do, and the fear of failure did not make for a relaxed and focused union. For others, the pressure to lose their virginity became overwhelming. Poor choices in partners, lack of awareness or experience in the use of birth control, and the ever-present fear of rejection were recipes for disaster.

Sex sells. Madison Avenue executives know this. Fortunes are made in advertising aimed at man's inherent appetite for sex. Weight loss, exercise, and hair loss prevention products have grown into giant industries with the primary aim of helping today's man stay sexually viable. In the past two or three years it has become impossible to escape the myriad clever and engaging commercials for medications that promise to eradicate "erectile dysfunction." It was an astute advertising executive who thought of saying, "Be sure to call your doctor if you experience priapism, an erection lasting more than four hours." Suddenly it's cool to have "ED," which reportedly affects 20 million men in the U.S. alone. Most of the advertising promotes only one aspect of a sexual relationship - the physical component. But what of the emotional, societal, or spiritual components?

One of the fastest growing industries in the world is internet pornography. Over 60% of all visits and commerce on the internet involve a sexual purpose (Schneider & Weiss, 2001). Voyeurism on an international stage, increasingly with "real-time" video and audio components, promotes intimacy without connection. Physical gratification for some becomes full-blown addiction for others. Often a seemingly harmless pastime, internet use can result in destroyed relationships, unfulfilling sex lives, and complete emotional, social, and financial wreckage, as well as loss of any reality base.

The following exercise is designed to help you examine your sexual beliefs, history, and fears.

Exercise: Your Sexual History

Answer the following questions in your journal:

1. Who taught you about sex?
2. How old were you when you had your first sexual experience?
3. How was sex treated in your family?
4. How many sexual partners have you had?
5. Did you ever coerce or force anyone to have sex with you?
6. Have you ever been forced or coerced into having sex with someone else?

Sexuality and Manhood

Joe is a patient at Our Lady of Perpetual Revenge Treatment Program and is completing his 28-day stay after detoxification. He's been sober for four weeks. His wife, Mary, is looking forward to Joe's coming home clean and sober for the first time in years. During family week at the treatment center, Mary asked about how sobriety might change their marital relationship, how it might impact on parenting issues, and how they could begin to develop greater intimacy and sexuality. Robert, the counselor, in all seriousness, told Mary and Joe to "keep your legs crossed for a period of time--we recommend a year--so that good, long-term sobriety can be established." Mary turns to Joe and thinks, "Hey, right! For the first time in ten years he'll be sober and we can have healthy sex again. And this jerk is telling us to keep our legs crossed? No way!" Joe is thinking, "It's show time. Time for Mary and me to play sexually, sober."

The way Robert and Our Lady staff treat sexuality is typical of many treatment centers, which give out either an incorrect or misleading message about sexuality, intimacy, and recovery. For many alcohol and drug abusers, sexuality has at best been buried under layers of pain and abuse. Telling them to "keep it buried" does not work. It is likely that many counselors approach sexuality in this way because they have had little or no training in sexuality. Sexologists and sex therapists have excellent training in how to deal with sexuality. Unfortunately, most of them admittedly know little about substance abuse. On the other hand, addiction counselors have excellent training and experience in dealing with alcohol and drug abuse, but little training in sex counseling. So alcohol and drug abuse counselors either rarely bring up the subject of sexuality in sessions, especially in early recovery, or, as in the case of Robert, provide misleading information and recommendations.

The interrelationship of alcohol use and sexual activity has been established for millennia. Moreover, there is widespread awareness that alcohol abuse can cause or exacerbate sexual problems. In fact, the rule should be: if you see one, look for the other. If a person is alcoholic, he/she will likely experience some sexual difficulties as well.

Sexual problems in alcoholics and drug abusers are multi-faceted, affecting all aspects of functioning. Because sexual problems may have an organic etiology, primary-care medicine as well as specialties such as urology, gynecology, and neurology need to be involved in screening, assessment, diagnosis, and treatment. The high incidence of physical trauma, such as rape or incest, among substance abusers means that legal professionals also are often included in the treatment process. The psychological and relational impacts of sexual problems of addicts involve social work, psychiatry, clinical psychology, and all forms of counseling (the "talk-therapies"). It is truly a problem with a multi-dimensional and interdisciplinary focus.

Alcoholism and drug abuse counseling, with its dual interest in achieving sobriety and abstinence and in the client's general emotional and relational health, can and should play a significant role in responding to the sexual problems of clients. Alcoholism professionals are in a unique position to insure that other disciplines are sensitive to the particular needs of the client and that services are provided in a manner that confronts the primary problem of addiction and enhances the person's potential for sobriety and recovery from addiction.

Addiction professionals can also be advocates for the creation of specific intervention programs for the alcoholic, his sexual partner, and other individuals such as family members and victims of sexual assault occurring under the influence of substances. The role addiction professionals can play in dealing with sexual problems of their clients is limited only by their lack of knowledge, experience, and clinical skills.

The following is a summary of sexual dysfunctions related to the use of particular drugs by men and women:

- Sedatives and hypnotics can result over time in depressed libido;
- Opioids can result in absent libido, decreased testosterone levels for men, and, concomitantly, impotence as well as increased prolactin levels;

- Cocaine has a bi-phasic effect; the person may initially feel sexually euphoric, but over time there is decreased libido, inhibited sexual desire, and impotence;
- Amphetamines can result in anorgasmia, with similar effects as with cocaine;
- Marijuana can decrease testosterone levels, contribute to gynecomastia, increase prolactin levels for men, and possibly promote fetal abnormalities.

The consumption of alcohol and drugs has an inverse relationship to sexual performance for men. The more one consumes, the lower one's ability to have an erection and orgasm. This phenomenon is not influenced by expectations, for although sexual desire for men is greatly affected by the setting and circumstances of alcohol consumption, the ability to perform does not improve with increased drinking. In sum, alcohol consumption results in a significant reduction in latency of penile tumescence (slower erections), decreased number of and rigidity of erections, and high rates of semi-erections. Thus, increased alcohol use leads to decreased libido and disinterest in one's sexual partner.

In addition, there is a tendency toward alcohol feminization in men. This is a result of gynecomastia and testicular atrophy due to either a disturbance of the hypothalamic-pituitary axis or peripheral changes in the man's liver functioning. The symptoms of gynecomastia are enlargement of the breasts, decrease in muscle tone and body hair, and a feminization of the pubic-hair area. The net result is changes in the gonadatropins. These changes in turn increase responsiveness to estrogen in men and decrease testosterone levels as well as penile tumescence and diameter, which then become insufficient for penetration in intercourse.

Impotence is not unique to alcoholic and drug-abusing men. All one need do is turn on the television almost any time of the day and watch commercials for ED, the new euphemistic way of speaking about "impotence." Twenty million American men have some form of erectile dysfunction. By the time the average man reaches 40 years of age he likely has experienced at least one episode of ED in his lifetime, most often as a result of over-consumption of alcohol, fatigue, stress, relational conflict, depression, or any number of emotional and psychological factors. Impotence is not uncommon for men. Thirty million men have experienced partial or temporary ED. By the age of 65 and over, 25% of men have sought help for impotence. Organic factors contribute to impotence in men as they age: vascular disease, diabetes, hypertension, kidney disease, MS, heavy smoking, pelvic trauma, spinal cord injury, and hormonal abnormalities.

It's been said that if you really want to know whether a man is experiencing impotence, ask his partner, not him. It is difficult for a man to say, "I am having trouble getting it up." Such a statement may be a blow to his ego. Besides, he may be too intoxicated even to know if he is having trouble with impotence.

Finally, there is a high correlation between the use of certain medications and impotence. These medications include anti-hypertensives, beta-blockers, psychiatric medications such as antidepressants and benzodiazepines, Phenobarbital, and Dilantin. All of these factors must be explored before a complete and reliable diagnosis of erectile dysfunction can be made.

Answer the following questions in your journal:

1. In what ways has your drug or alcohol use affected your sex life?

2. How has a diminished or diminishing libido affected your self-esteem?

3. How has a diminished or diminishing libido affected your relationship with your significant other(s)?

4. In what ways, if any, might you benefit from a diminished libido?

CHAPTER EIGHT
The Male Spiritual Journey

I live my life in growing orbits
Which move out over the things of the world.
Perhaps I can never achieve the last,
But that will be my attempt.
I am circling around God, around the ancient tower,
And I have been circling for a thousand years,
And I still don't know if I am a falcon, or a storm,
or a great song.
Rainer Maria Rilke

Before enlightenment
chopping wood
carrying water

After enlightenment
chopping wood
carrying water
Zen Proverb

There are two major spiritual tasks men face: discovering what you are to be and moving into a deeper inner life, with a sense of self and the world. The two essential questions in life for men are how to live and why. It is as simple (and complex) as that. The temptation is to wallpaper the empty spaces of our lives with work, not providing the necessary balance among service, work, and avocation. But the true male spiritual journey is to grow in grace, not just in doing more things.

Male spirituality involves not just one compartment of life, but the deepest dimension of who we were made to be, our ultimate questions, hopes, fears, and loves. It gives us meaning in living by addressing life's questions of self-worth and significance. It reveals the mysteries of living, the realization that life's ultimate meaning cannot lie in speed, youth, consumerism, achievement, and physical beauty as defined by our culture.

This chapter explores the male spiritual journey. It first explores the downward journey calling us to face our limits and wounds, the essential journey of letting go of control. The journey takes us into our desert spaces, the alone times where we confront who we are and our True Self. The chapter then turns to the interplay between the outward and inward components of the journey, to finding new sources of joy and refreshment in life. This involves getting in touch with something greater than ourselves.

Men recoil from the idea of going downward for we fear descent and decline. We fear we will be insignificant when removed from the power, possessions, and prestige that drive us.

In the first part of a man's journey he finds himself filled with ascent, being in control. In the second half of life a man goes inward, giving up his efforts to control, digging deeper to new sources of refreshment. To get there he must go through his brokenness and woundedness.

Male spirituality is primarily a journey of limitation, realizing we cannot have it all, of seeing the limits of our power and the language of our pain. The journey takes us through the dark night of the soul of pain to trust. All men experience some pain through wounds in relationship, career setbacks, physical illness, and death of friends and colleagues. What we do with that pain determines how we will live.

Digging deeper requires alone time in the desert with periods of feeling lost. We don't like to be lost; after all, we are problem solvers who never ask for directions. Be careful of the man who tells you life is one joy after another with no desert times. He is fooling himself. Male spirituality involves time in the desert, darkness, wilderness, where we are reborn into something new and wonderful.

The desert is not just a place but also a state of being. Most of our daily lives are filled with blasts of the boring and ordinary. Yet, in the deserted, abandoned part of our day, when we feel most alone, we face the ultimate question of life, "Why am I here?"

Further, the dark night of the soul is not always a dread-filled and depressing experience. The real meaning of the term "dark night of the soul" is that things may be obscure. We cannot see or grasp what is happening. It is a sense of unknowing, of mystery. In those dark times of the desert we need to trust someone else to be our guide.

Spirituality based on brokenness demands rethinking of what it means to be a man. We are not our faults, the diseases of our body, being a father, husband, and employee. The fact is we are more than these. Who we are is unchangeable; that does not get lost when age, disease, or circumstances change. Finding out who we are will lead us to the work we need to do, the lessons we need to learn.

The answers come when we measure ourselves by something other than performance, despite what others tell us. We will be incessantly restless until we turn all our woundedness into health, our deformity into beauty, and our embarrassment into laughter.

Male spirituality is always about letting go of a false sense of independence. As youths, we fought for our independence. Dependence meant anxiety, fear, illness, failing, infirmity, and the risk of exploitation. For younger men, dependence meant inferiority. "Stand on your own two feet. Act like a man. Do it yourself, don't bother with anybody else, you do not need anyone." Through most of our lives we sought to manage our finances, our households, our career. To be a man was to be self-sufficient.

Yet we never were fully independent. We live in a world that is connected to everything that has lived, lives, and will live. To let go is to acknowledge we are interdependent on others. We never were in control, despite all of our efforts.

Central to the inward journey is a sense of continuity of life with something greater than ourselves. The great spiritual truth is that anyone's life is not just about him. There is a far greater story being played out. Our task in the inward journey is to discover our role in that greater story.

Case Studies: Paul, Michael, Bob, and John

Instead of one extended case study, this section will briefly tell the stories of the spiritual journeys of several men at different stages of life.

Paul is eighty-two years old and describes himself as a religious mutt. He was raised Catholic, practices Buddhism zazen and Chinese Qigong, and works in an ecumenical organization. He oozes warmth, compassion, wonder, and grace in all he says and does. Yet, he readily confesses that his personal journey has not been easy. He has dealt with the demons of his alcoholism and his compulsive behavior, his workaholism, and his physical infirmities. Sober now for thirty years, Paul confesses that he has been to his own personal hell and back. He has had many journeys downward to confront his shadow, his false self. Paul will also tell you that without this downward journey he perhaps never would have found his True Self, his essential spiritual nature.

Michael is thirty and tells of his dark night of the soul, when the company he owned went through several audits. A consultant to a major accounting firm reviewed the company books and erroneously concluded that there was fraud and that Michael would be charged with the errors and likely sent to jail. For days Michael wandered aimlessly in the prison of his fears and terror only to find out the accountant was totally in error. Michael was guilty of no wrongdoing and his anxiety was ill founded. The accusation had shaken him to his core and forced him to examine his beliefs and values. What would he be without his career? What was he if not a free man? The terror of that time did not go away easily, and left him seeking a deeper meaning.

Bob, forty-nine, said, "I once thought life was one continuous party, filled with great happiness and very few sorrows. Then my sister died of breast cancer at thirty-six. My son was born with a hearing disability and my wife was in a serious auto accident that has left her in constant pain. Now I wrestle with the thought that life may just be one sorrow after another. I want to find a balance in my life between joys, which still are many, and sorrows, which seem to come in waves. Why can't life be simple, either happiness or sadness, rather than this living with both?" This was Bob's spiritual quandary, prompted by a series of tragic events in his immediate family.

John, twenty-seven, said, "I thought I was doing fine spiritually until my best friend from college, Jack, died at twenty-nine of a heart attack. I became cynical and resentful of people with their seemingly easy lives. My spirituality was rocked as I was angry with God. How could God allow my friend to die so young, leaving behind a wife and child? It was not until I fully grieved my friend's death that I was able to begin again my conversations with God. Now I see how the outward event of my friend's death was an essential, albeit painful, part of my inward spiritual journey."

These case studies pose another question: Is it necessary to go through such extreme terrors, traumas, and tragedies as these characters did to have a spiritual transformation? How can men who have not endured such dramatic experiences undertake their spiritual journeys?

The following exercises are intended to take the reader through his own spiritual journey, reflecting key issues and questions as a step toward spiritual discovery for men who may or may not have been compelled to examine their lives and spiritual selves as the characters in the case studies were. The reader is encouraged to complete each exercise separately in his journal.

Exercise: A Spiritual Inventory

Respond to these statements as honestly as possible. You may experience the following in your daily life. If so, how often? (1= many times a day, 2 = every day, 3 = most days, 4 = some days, 5 = once in a while, 6 = never or almost never)

1. I feel a presence of something greater than myself (Spirit, Higher Power, God).

2. I experience a connection to all of life.

3. At times (in nature, in community, in worshipful times) I feel a joy that lifts me out of my daily concerns.

4. I find strength and comfort in my faith, my religion, and my spiritual life.

5. I feel deep inner peace or harmony when....

6. I ask for help from my Higher Power, God, in the midst of daily activities.

7. I feel guided by my Higher Power in the midst of daily activities.

8. I feel love for me from something greater than myself.

9. I feel that love for me through others.

10. The beauty of creation spiritually touches me. I feel thankful and grateful for my blessings.

11. I feel a selfless caring for others.

12. I desire to be closer to and in union with my Higher Power.

13. In general, I feel close to something greater than myself.

Now, answer these questions:

1. What emotional or physical pain do you still have?

2. How have you transformed your pain?

3. How do you continue to transmit your pain to others or yourself?

4. Who are you today; what you have come to believe you are?

5. How do you fit into the grand scheme of things?

6. Where do you feel significant?

7. What gives you a sense of meaning and purpose in your life?

8. What have been a few of your joys and sorrows in life? How have these joys and sorrows shaped you?

9. Where have you experienced the winning power of love in your life?

10. What control are you still seeking to maintain?

11. Do you have the courage to change what you can change?

12. What do you need to let go of today?

13. Do you have the serenity to accept what you cannot change?

14. Do you have the wisdom to know the difference between what you can change and what you cannot?

CHAPTER NINE
Work

All times are one if heart delight
In work, if hands join the world right.
Wendell Barry, From the Distance

My grandfather once told me that there are two kinds of people: those who work and those who take credit. He told me to try to be in the first group; there's less competition there.
Indira Gandhi (1917-1984)

Work defines most men. When we meet another man one of the first questions we'll ask is: "What do you do for a living?" We ask this question because, for most of us, our jobs are our identity, the measure of our self-worth and a central part of our lives. Work connects us to reality. For many of us, our work is all there is. Work may be our job description of life. The question "What do you do for a living?" also identifies who we are and is a way of measuring ourselves against others, telling others something about our status, and defining our worth in the world of other men. We are told that we can easily be replaced and are often taken advantage of by our work. We believe we are expendable, and this insecurity drives us to go beyond what may be "healthy" emotionally for us. Work is the playing field where we fulfill the honored and respected roles of provider, protector, and producer. If a man chooses to not follow this path in his adulthood, he is often rejected and shamed. These "anti-men" attitudes are widely accepted in the culture and rarely challenged. Men carry a heavy sense of physical responsibility for provision and protection, and this takes a serious toll on our health and our zest for life. We often destroy our relationships and give our children less "just being with" time (which is what they need from us) because of our work. We work too hard. The amount of time men spend at work seems to be ever-increasing. Eventually we may get to a point in life when we see that we have sacrificed everything on work's altar and that we are not just our profit-and-loss statements or our career ambitions.

So, many of us need to find new joy in our work. To find what brings you joy at work, you will need to turn in another direction, to the inner reflection held by the image you have found. This may require a moment of sobering self-reflection. In his poem "The Half Turn of Your Face," David Whyte speaks of that moment when you face yourself as you are, yet remember your reflection in the mirror, that which you loved when you were younger and trusted everything you wanted. In that moment you make a half turn of your face to what matters now to you.

The Half Turn of Your Face
by David Whyte

The half turn of your face
toward truth
is the one movement
you will not make.

After all
having seen it before.
You wouldn't
want
to take that
path again.

And have to greet
yourself
as you are
and tell yourself

what it was like
to have come so far
and all in vain.

But most of all
to remember how it felt again
to see
reflected
in your own mirror
the lines of abandonment
and loss.
And have those words spoken
inviting you back,
The ones you used to say,
The ones you loved
when your body was young
and you trusted
everything you wanted.

Hard to look,
but you know it has to happen
and
that it takes
only the half turn of your face
to scare yourself to the core.
Seeing again
that strange resolve in your new reflection.

Printed with permission from Many Rivers Press, Langley, Washington.
www.davidwhyte.com

"The Half Turn of Your Face" is a powerful, compelling concept. It applies so well to finding one's true vocation. It can also be applied on a broader scale to many of the questions explored in this book, such as discovering one's spiritual self or finding meaning in any dimension of one's life. Be open to thinking about other ways to make the half turn in the course of self-discovery.

Case studies: Phillip and Kevin

Phillip made the "half turn of his face" at the age of 51 when he ended an 18-year career as a minister of a church to try his hand at music writing. Although he continues to support himself as an interim clergyman, his real passion is writing music. He had once been asked, "If someone gave you $100,000 a year and you need not worry about making ends meet, what you would do?" Without any hesitation Phillip responded, "Write music." In that moment he began to make the half turn of his face toward what brought him joy. He was "scared to the core," in David Whyte's words, by the challenges of this half turn of his face, but saw a new reflection of who he was becoming.

Kevin was a 45-year-old lawyer with a successful practice in Asheville, North Carolina. He had never been married and has no children. As he looked into the mirror of his life he asked himself, "Is that all there is?" When he made the half turn of his face, the answer to his question was, "No, I want to give back to society in a different way. I want to work in the helping professions." He left his law practice and returned to school for a degree in social work. He now works in a shelter for homeless men. He feels a new sense of significance, not in material terms but in the legacy of compassion he is leaving behind in the lives of the men he helps.

Perhaps it is time to have another outlook on work, to find what fulfills your inner needs. In *Anam* Cara, John O'Donohue tells a wonderful story about a Zen monk in Japan. The emperor had a magnificent, ancient vase that fell and broke into thousands of pieces. The pieces were gathered up and the emperor summoned all of the best potters in the kingdom to reassemble the vase. One by one each fai led and was beheaded for the failure. Weeks went by and all of the best potters in the land had been killed. One Zen monk remained. His young apprentice gathered the pieces together and brought them to his master. Finally the monk reassembled the vase, and it was truly beautiful. The emperor was delighted and graciously rewarded the monk.

One day, the monk's young apprentice came across fragments of the vase that were never used in the reassembly. He asked the monk how he was able to make the vase so beautiful without these fragments. The Zen master said, "If you do the work that you do with a loving heart, then you will always be able to make something beautiful." (O'Donohue, 1998)

Downshifting

Here are other stories men tell about how they view work. Tom says, "I am bored in my job. But here I am, fifty-two, and I'll be working into my late sixties. I have a young son who will be entering college when I am sixty-five years old. Retirement? Not for a long time." Carl, fifty-four, says, "I am earning a million dollars a year as a corporate president. I hate my job, but I am scared to death of losing it. If I do, I will not be able to live in the manner to which my family and I have grown accustomed." Stanley says, "I am fifty-eight and have had a good career as a writer. I have no regrets about my career choices. But I have been doing freelance work all my life and now face my elder years without any pension or retirement plan, nothing to fall back on in the future. Now what am I to do?"

For some, they want to downshift, to work fewer hours or with less responsibility or pressure. Here are steps you can take to change your work pattern:

- Keep lunchtime personal. Stop grabbing the sandwich at the cafeteria and chowing down at your desk amidst piles of paper and e-mails.
- Take a walk at lunchtime; eat slowly. The work will still be there when you return.
- Avoid weekend business travel. Make firm personal appointments.
- Set reasonable deadlines. Set stop times.
- Declare your priority for family. This may be hard, as work may have been the number one priority in your life. What would it mean to put family and self first instead of work?
- Negotiate extra vacation time. Arrange flextime. Go part-time.
- Make a lateral or downward move. Decline a promotion.

- Telecommute.
- Take early or gradual retirement.

Case Study: Bruce

Bruce was a successful electrician with a solid book of business. He learned the electrical trade after high school and started his own business in his twenties. He was financially successful, happily married, and his children were grown. Yet Bruce knew there was more to life than money in the bank and saving for retirement. At fifty-eight, Bruce decided he needed to downshift, to work less and put in fewer hours. He met with his accountant and found a way to cash in and access his retirement funds early. He sold his business and bought a house in the Mexican mountains. From there he did electrical contracting jobs in Mexico and the United States. As a hedge against his fear of not having enough, he opened a small business in Boulder, Colorado, and lived half of the year in Mexico and the other half in Colorado. Bruce soon learned that he did not need the Colorado business and that his life was very full in Mexico. He "retired" to work only in Mexico.

Bruce downshifted in two steps from a full-time business to more relaxed work. Bruce now picks and chooses the work that gives him energy and passion. He has been an inspiration to many of us. Downshifting does not necessarily mean that you stop working entirely; rather, it means that you focus on what you want to do, not just what you need to do.

Exercise I: The role of work in your life

Answer these questions:

1. How do you introduce yourself at a party?
2. What is this lure of work for you?
3. What has work become for you?
4. What is the toll of today's workplace on you?
5. What would you do if you did not have to work? If you were given your salary for a year and were able to take a sabbatical, what would you do? Most

importantly, what questions would you want answered during your sabbatical?

6. Have you become your work?

7. Is work an escape from other parts of your life, into a world under your control?

8. Do you feel as if you have climbed the ladder of success only to realize that the ladder is leaning against the wrong building?

9. Do you sometimes feel lost at work? Have you experienced an internal sticker shock, seeing that the price you paid for career advancement was your vitality, passion, and commitments?

Exercise II: Workplace robbers

Review the following list of workplace robbers and ask yourself whether any of them are issues or concerns for you at work.

- Competitive pressures. Do you feel you have to do more to gain someone's approval or because someone else is there behind you desiring your job?

- The corporate culture. Do you put in extra hours on evenings, weekends, or holidays just to keep up? Do you feel as if you have to do more with less?

- The need to "make the numbers." Do you feel pressured to meet sales quotas or profit benchmarks, to do better? Do you feel the pressure to serve more people?

- Rapid change. Are you running as fast as you can but never able to keep up with the pace of change?

- Overwhelming work burdens. Is there too much to do and not enough time to do it? What has work become for you? Are you rusted out at work? Have you lost the fire and passion you once had?

Exercise III: Finding fulfilling work

Answer the following questions:

1. What were you created to be in life?

2. Is what you are currently doing that thing for which you were created?

3. What aspects of your current work fulfill your "destiny"?

4. What can you bring into your work that enlivens and perhaps even scares you a little?

Exercise IV: The Circle Game

Step #1: Draw a large circle on half a page in your journal. In that circle write down the qualities you can express in your current work. For example, it might be your creativity, your skills, your passion and compassion, the joys and problems of working with people, etc.

Step #2:

Write below the circle the qualities you would like to express in life. These may be qualities such as expressing love, making an impact on others, being a change agent, leaving a record of your creativity, having a sense of peace, quiet and joy, participating in a spiritual journey to serenity, finding more leisure time, etc.

Step #3:

Which of these qualities can be expressed in your current work? Write them inside the circle at the top. Which qualities cannot be expressed in your current work environment? Now write these qualities outside the circle. As you look over what is inside and outside the circle, mark the three items that are most important to you at this point in your life. How can you bring into your work those items outside the circle that are most important to you? The essence of work is to find at work what you truly love to do. When these qualities cannot be brought into your work, you need to find a way to make them part of your life as a whole.

Exercise V: Finding Your Calling

In the case studies earlier in this chapter, Philip, Kevin, and Bruce not only heard the drum of their calling but were able to manage the monetary costs of the career change foretold by the beat. For others, like Carl and Tom, the chronic pain of their chosen careers was becoming unbearable, with no relief in sight. How do we find our calling, especially if it has been buried under heaps of activities over time? One way to hear that drum is to conduct a job interview of ourselves.

- First, finding your heartbeat begins in stillness. Get away from the chatter around you and retreat to aloneness, where you can listen to the voice of your soul that says, "Do this. This is what you were meant to be." Bubbling up from deep within you, listen to the stillness that calls you back to your dreams.
- Listen to the yearnings that sneak up on you in subtle ways. You may be watching a movie and something grabs you, saying, "Pay attention to this. This is important."
- Figure out what this calling will cost you and people in your life. Ask yourself what you are willing to pay in time, money, and emotions to respond to this calling.

Now answer these questions in your journal:

1. What do you feel called to do at this stage of your life?
2. What gives you a sense of wholeness in life? When you find it, that is likely your calling.
3. What parts of you have gone undeveloped or underdeveloped in your life and work thus far? It is those parts of you that have been lost in the shadows that may now be seeking light.
4. What is still waiting to be born in you?
5. What would be incomplete in your life if you never did this one thing?

Exercise VI: Number Your Days: Having a Sense of Wonder and Gratitude

Building on the previous exercises, let's take this experience of self-exploration to another level. This exercise extends and enlarges the inquiry, putting work in the broader context of life satisfaction.

- List the things that have given you the greatest joys in life.
- Focus on each of the people and joyful events in each period of your life.
- List the times you have felt awe and the circumstances that brought that about.
- Make this week, month, or year a celebration of your life by making a pilgrimage to a significant place of joy in your life. Plan a special day

to celebrate your life. Help someone else celebrate the joys of their life story.

- Put together an album of photos and mementos of joyous and wondrous times in your life.
- Visit and talk with people from your past who gave you perspective on different aspects of your life. Celebrate your roots by attending an ethnic festival. Read poetry or prose from your heritage. Listen to its music.
- List the conflicts of your life that have taught you something important. Conduct an internal dialogue with the ones that seem most significant.
- Give yourself a day of fun. A time of wonder and joy.

CHAPTER TEN
Money

I'm living so far beyond my income that we may almost be said to be living apart.
e e cummings
US poet (1894 - 1962)

What is it about men and money? It is generally the last frontier we will ever cross or talk about with others. Men talk about money in code. Instead of coming right out and asking, "So, how much do you make for a living?" or "What's your net worth?" we ask, "So, what do you do for a living?" using work as a measuring stick to determine indirectly what a man earns. If a man tells you he is a laborer or a CEO, you can generally have some idea what he is worth, how much he makes.

Money means many things to men: power, possessions, prestige, perks, and possibilities. For women, money can mean other things: security, the ability to make purchases for themselves and family members, what one needs to do the things one wants to do.

Since work and money play significant roles in the lives of many men, it is important to address these issues. Work is central to most men's lives and essentially defines them. It is important to take a fresh look at work and money to find out what we really love, to find a new voice at work, and to act out of passion for all we do.

We work because work connects us to reality. We earn because it provides a measurement of how we are related to that reality, especially if power, possessions, and prestige are important to us. Money brings us alive, giving meaning to what we do. For many, money is all there is. Money and work may be how we identify ourselves, what we do "for a living." Some men have become their job description. There is a humorous gravestone in London that reads, "Here lies Jeremy Brown, born a man and died a grocer." To test this out, go to a cocktail party or a gathering of men. "What do you do for a living?" is one of the first questions men ask each other. In recent years this has also increasingly become the case for women--a big difference from a few decades ago. Women still have alternatives to a work-based identity that men don't, but at the same time they are fighting to have the "homemaker" role recognized as real work that merits compensation. The explicit question "What do you do for a living?" and the implicit question "How much do you earn?" identify who we are and are means of measuring ourselves against others. Money defines our worth in what we think of as the world of men.

However, we are not just what our resumes say we are. We are not our profit-and-loss statements. Perhaps we see how work and money have become the sum of our identity as we sacrificed everything on the corporate altar. Max, a 51-year-old plumber, says, "My work is my life. I would not know how else to describe myself if not in terms of what I do. In fact, it is frightening to think about my identity and sense of significance after I stop working. What will that be like?"

Why do we continue to slog through work that leaves us feeling empty?
- The promise of a pension somewhere in the future--the "gold watch" syndrome
- The desire, however misguided, still to ascend the work ladder of success--the "be all you can be" syndrome
- The bills still need to be paid--the "I cannot afford to quit" syndrome
- A gnawing sense that we still do not have enough, whatever "enough" means to us--the "I want it all" syndrome
- A sense of security--the "I'm safe and secure now" syndrome.

Money may mean that we are able to buy the things that we and our family desire, or think we desire. Until recently, we identified our needs and then saved money until we could make the purchases. This gave work a sense of meaning. Work may not have been satisfying, but at least it had an identifiable purpose that was likely appreciated at home, at the workplace, or in society as a whole. Today, seeking instant gratification of our needs, we buy on credit. As a result, money is detached from the item initially purchased and becomes merely a way of paying off credit-card debt. Today, it often feels like a never-ending cycle of work and spending: the mortgage, kids' college education, saving for retirement, our "toys," and, for some, child support or alimony.

Affluenza

Some men (and women) suffer from a common ailment: affluenza; we have too much and yet want more. Simply defined, affluenza is a dysfunctional relationship with or pursuit of money/wealth. Globally, it is a back-up in the flow of money resulting in a polarization of the classes and a loss of economic and emotional balance. We can see the symptoms of affluenza throughout our culture: in those around us who have wealth, in those who are pursuing wealth, and in varying degrees within ourselves. A clinical definition is:

- The collective addictions, character flaws, psychological wounds, neuroses, and behavioral disorders caused or exacerbated by the presence of or desire for money/wealth.
- In corporations and businesses it manifests as a loss of personal and professional productivity, high turnover rate among CEOs and employees, and an increase in sick days.
- In individuals it takes the form of a dysfunctional or unhealthy relationship with money, regardless of one's socio-economic level. It manifests as behaviors resulting from a preoccupation with--or imbalance around--the money in our lives.
- The psychological dysfunctions of affluenza within the family are generational; they are frequently passed from parent to child.

The symptoms of affluenza are:
- A loss of personal and professional productivity
- A loss of future motivation
- An inability to delay gratification or tolerate frustration
- A false sense of entitlement
- Low self-esteem

- Low self-worth
- Loss of self-confidence
- Preoccupation with externals
- Depression
- Self-absorption
- High regard for outer self/low regard for inner self
- "Survivor's" guilt/shame
- Sudden wealth syndrome
- Sudden poverty syndrome
- Workaholism
- Addictions
- Other compulsive-addictive behaviors: i.e., rampant materialism and consumerism

The psychological dynamics of affluenza are more complex, and more harmful, than one popularized definition of affluenza as merely "a rich person's disease." People across all socio-economic levels buy into the overriding value our culture places on money, the assumption that money solves all problems. Thus, denial of money-related difficulties is supported by society, and many sufferers of affluenza hesitate to seek help.

Affluenza can be successfully overcome. With personal insight into the potentially crippling effects that the obsession with money can have on every aspect of our lives--professionally and personally--we can begin to create our own monetary intentions and employ our money in more appropriate ways. As employees we can learn how to create emotional balance around financial matters in the work environment, resulting in a more successful business and--most importantly--a more balanced and successful lifestyle.

Case Studies: Roger, Carl, and Jim

This section will provide vignettes of several men to illustrate how they look at money.

Roger is the CEO of a Fortune 500 company. His estimated income in 1990 was twenty-six million dollars, not bad for a man who barely finished college and inherited his company from his father. He lived in a mansion in Greenwich, Connecticut, and flew weekly in the corporate jet to his "castle" home in Florida, which stretched from the Atlantic Ocean to the Intracoastal Waterway.

One night this author (David) was visiting Roger and his wife as a guest in their Florida home. After a delicious meal prepared by a 5-star chef, we relaxed in their "den" and retired early. Awakened around midnight by noise in the kitchen, I went downstairs to see what was going on. There, in the kitchen, Roger and his wife were going over their checkbook, paying bills. I said to Roger's wife, Jean, "Why are you doing that, Jean? You could hire a room full of accountants to do your checkbook." Jean responded, "We don't trust anyone else with our personal checkbook." I was astonished and retired to bed, having seen that money does not necessarily bring peace of mind.

A second case is Carl, an Executive Vice President of another Fortune 500 company. He was earning over one million dollars a year, not counting stock options. One year the business was undergoing major financial problems and the Board of Directors was exploring changes in their management structure. Carl was worried he'd lose his job. In a conversation I had with Carl he expressed his anxiety about being out of work.

Carl said, "I am worried I will lose my job. I am fifty years old, with a huge mortgage and family to support. Who will hire me?" When asked about the source of his anxiety. Carl's response was, "If I should lose my job I might not be able to provide the life style my wife and family are accustomed to." With a net worth of tens of millions, he was fearful that he'd have to cut back his spending. Carl and his family truly suffered from "affluenza."

Jim is a laborer, barely getting by on thirty-five thousand dollars a year. His wife worked as a maid in a hotel, and their combined annual income barely exceeded fifty thousand dollars, from which he had to pay his mortgage, expenses, and looming college tuition bills for his two children. Despite all this, Jim and his wife Sue were quite contented with their life and felt little fear about the loss of their income. Although work was spotty for Jim, he rested at night with the assurance that "everything will be OK." Jim said to me, "We have little, we need little, yet we know all will be well. We will not be out on the street. There is food on the table, we are a closely knit family, we love each other dearly, and life is good."

These three men have very different attitudes about money, net worth, and security. The point is not that accumulation of wealth is not a good thing, or that poverty or living close to the poverty line is to be desired. Instead, happiness is in the eyes of the beholder. The key question every man needs to ask himself is, "How much would I be worth if I lost all of my money?" The answer to that question might determine one's level of peace, anxiety, security, and happiness. After all, it is not happy (or wealthy) people that are grateful but grateful people that are happy. Or in the words of the great philosophers John Lennon and Paul McCartney, "Money can't buy you love."

Do you find yourself often reflecting on your net worth and assets? Do you keep mental tally sheets of what you have accumulated so far? Do you hire a financial planner to assure you that there is enough for the future? The following exercises may illuminate your position on money.

Exercise I: Do you have Affluenza?
Diagnose yourself using the key below.
1. I'm willing to pay more for a t-shirt if it has a cool corporate logo on it.
2. I believe that if I buy the expensive suit, the promotion will come.
3. I have a tie collection Donald Trump would envy.
4. When I'm cold, I take my clothes off and turn up the heat.
5. I'm willing to work 40 years at a job I hate so I can buy lots of stuff.
6. When I'm feeling blue, I like to go on e-bay and treat myself.
7. I want a sport utility vehicle, although I rarely drive in conditions that warrant having one.
8. I usually make just the minimum payment on my credit cards.
9. I believe that whoever dies with the most toys wins.
10. Most of the things my friends/family and I enjoy doing together are free.

11. I don't measure my self-worth (or that of others) by what I own.

12. I know how to pinch a dollar until it screams.

13. I worry about the effects of advertising on children.

14. To get to work, I carpool, ride my bike, or use public transportation.

15. I'd rather be golfing right now.

For questions 1-9 and 15, give yourself 2 points for true and 1 point for false. For questions 10-14, give yourself 0 points for true and 2 points for false.

If you scored:

10-15: No dangerous signs of affluenza at this time.

16-22: Warning: You have mild affluenza.

23-30: Cut up your credit cards and call a doctor immediately!

Exercise II: Your spiritual financial journey
Step #1:

Imagine yourself setting out on a journey. During this journey, you are in search of the qualities in your life that you still want to find. What "lands and destinations" do you still seek to visit? Think both about geographic and life milestones as "destinations" for yourself. For example, are there places in the world you want to see? Are there adventures you still wish to experience? What areas of significance and meaning do you still wish to have in your world? Are there emotional, physical, and social events or experiences you still want to have in your life's journey? Where would you still like to go in your career and profession?

Write down the work "destinations" where you still wish to go, the journey you still want to take in your life.

Step #2:

What do you really need for the journey? How much money do you really need to enjoy the journey? What would you need to take along on this trip? Personal possessions, music to listen to, books to read, people you wish to be with, sacred objects, etc.? What other items would you bring, such as social, emotional, and spiritual qualities? List at least fourteen items below.

Step #3:

Follow the old rule in packing for a trip: take what you have packed and cut that in half. You probably packed too much already. You have more than you will ever need for your life's journey. Cut the above list in half, down to no more than seven items.

Step #4:

Having done that, cut it again, down to three items. What are the three most important items you will need for your journey?

Those are probably all you will need for the rest of your life's journey in work. This may be a difficult and painful exercise, casting off the power, possessions, and work prestige you have accumulated so far. But in all likelihood you do not need these any more. In fact, they may be an impediment to your life's journey at work. Your preoccupation with these items can weigh you down.

CHAPTER ELEVEN
Men and Their Children

By the time a man realizes that maybe his father was right, he usually has a son who thinks he's wrong.
Charles Wadsworth

The only words and actions that I want to transmit to others are those which come from the right view, right thinking and right speech. I vow to live the present moment in such a way that I can guarantee a bright future for my descendants.
Thich Nhat Hanh

The father-child bond, especially the father-son bond, may be the most significant relationship in a man's life. It is essential that you explore this relationship on your journey, because many men carry strong feelings both about their own fathers and about their role as fathers to their children. And even if a man has no biological children of his own, in many cases he may be a stepfather to someone else's children, may be thinking of one day being a father, or may have feelings about what it might be like to be a father. It is essential for a man to understand the role that his own father has played in his life. If he has a son, it is important to explore how to be a spiritual father and how to be a healthy parent.

First, it is important to acknowledge that there are many other variations of the father-child relationship: the single father, the stepfather, fathers with multiple families, the gay father, and so forth. So we do not want to imply that fathering involves only the traditional father-son relationship.

One of the beauties of life today is that there does not seem to be a uniform pattern to fit all men. We are all making it up as we go along.

A man can help his sons and daughters by sharing his inner life with them, by being open with his thoughts, feelings, dreams, and hurts. As a way of preparing his sons for manhood, a man can telecast the journey he has been through to inform and coach his sons through their eventual journey. If a man is in recovery from addiction, this is especially important as we know alcoholism and drug abuse runs in families.

When a man's children get to different stages of their lives, they likely will remember the stories of their father's wounding and how he wrestled with it. Perhaps they will consult with their father for guidance through that journey. If a man's sons received good masculine energy from their father as they grew up, they likely will not reject it when they are grown. A positive male figure can teach a boy how to be a man in a healthy, balanced sense.

Most importantly, a child needs to believe that his father respects and admires him. He wants his dad to be proud of him. As he grows into adulthood a father's pride may seem patronizing if a foundation of appreciation and praise was not laid in childhood. What a boy needs all along is not just his parent's approval (which we hope most boys receive), but adult respect and honest admiration. The honoring of the man in the boy is what invites the boy into the club of men. This lets him know that he is his father's equal.

To be a mature father, a man can also teach his sons and daughters lessons or virtues such as self-possession, truthfulness, responsibility, closure, and challenge. *Self-possession* is the virtue of self-knowledge. It is the ability to be in touch with one's center, feelings, and motives. A self-possessed man has self-knowledge and awareness. He knows (as well as any of us realistically can) where he is coming from and where he is going. He seeks the well being of others and not simply what he wants for himself.

Another virtue is *truthfulness,* which is reality knowledge. It is one's ability to see clearly what is going on in the world. Truthfulness means being able to name truth. This virtue presupposes that a man is objective and detached from the situation being viewed. It means that he has balanced judgment and does not simply project his own biases and prejudices onto the reality. Sometimes a man has to be truthful about things with which he is emotionally involved. This can be difficult and requires wisdom and maturity.

Third, *responsibility* is the opposite of passivity. Another term for this might be "initiative." A responsible father does not need to be told what to do; he does it and assumes responsibility for his actions. This does not mean "shooting from the hip" or being a "ready, fire, aim" guy. It means taking appropriate action when needed.

Closure is the strength needed to make a decision when a decision must be made. It is an essential element of responsible decision-making. It requires the wisdom of Kenny Rogers to "know when to hold 'em and when to fold 'em. Know when to walk away, know when to run."

Finally, *challenge* might be called "tough love." If forgiveness is the ability to let go of hurts, challenge is the ability to risk hurting. This is not negative or destructive action, but action always guided by love. It requires forthrightness. Challenge means being willing to risk argument, misunderstanding, and disagreement, being willing to stick your neck out for a person or a value in which you believe.

Today many children live with their parents long after they are grown because they cannot afford to live anywhere else. There is now an opportunity for fathers to learn how to nurture their children. Fathers have to be willing to suspend decades of cultural conditioning and learn how to be nurturers as well as providers. They need to learn the language of the heart; to feel what a child feels and to acknowledge the truth of those feelings, without feeling (or acting on) the urge to correct, punish, or reward. Today, younger fathers are making great strides in learning how to nurture their children and deriving personal benefits from these life changes. Even a father with a late-life baby can transform his behavior.

Fatherhood has as significant an impact on mental and physical health as career achievement does. Research shows that fathers who are highly invested in their work but who also care about their children and spend significant time with them can still have an important effect on the emotional well-being of their sons and daughters and, by extension, on their own emotional well-being. The most promising direction for redefining masculinity lies in reinventing fatherhood. Most of the reinvented fathers are now in their twenties and thirties, but not all. Some are Start-Over Dads in their late forties and fifties, raising second families.

Most men in their fifties were not brought up to be warm, sensitive fathers. They could not look to their dads as role models for nurturing. Most were taught to separate quickly from their parents and move away. No doubt many men today did not have fathers who were models of caring, emotional expressiveness, and involvement with their children.

These generational contrasts are valid up to a point, but as with any generalization, there are exceptions. Many men who came of age in the 1960s were part of a generation that did separate quickly from parents and move away, in part because they were trying to live by different values from their parents' and thus could not identify closely with their fathers. But one expression of their generation's idealism was to try to be parents in different ways--to be more available, "soft," and nurturing--and thereby avoid the kinds of conflicts they had had with their parents. Breaking down gender roles, with fathers more actively present in childrearing and sharing both the burden and the positive experience more equally with mothers, was part of this cultural evolution. There are many men, now in their fifties and sixties, who were that kind of father, and not just the second time around, but also in their 30's and perhaps 20's (although many baby boomers had children late, so it is likely that they were more mature and thoughtful when they began as parents). On a recent radio program about "Generation Y" (the children of baby boomers), it was observed that these young people often regard their parents as "good friends." That's one reason (besides economic necessity) why they more often live with their parents than the students and young adults of the 1960s did. So some credit must be given to the 1960s-70s counterculture for changing values and practices in parenting.

Fathers play critical roles in the lives of their children:

1. Fathers can provide reciprocal *nurturing* that is critical in early development of children. Although nurturing is commonly associated with the mother's role, fathers too need to nurture their children through expressions of love and caring.

2. Fathers can be *role models*. Children need positive male role models whom they can admire and emulate.

3. Fathers *initiate boys into manhood.* Traditionally this initiation happened through an experience of the wonders of nature and by the boy facing his

frailties and limitations. Vision quests and bar mitzvahs were traditional initiation rites. Initiation moves a young man from a natural self-centeredness to a more mature, healthy inclusion of others. This becomes a critical factor in helping to ensure success later in life. A man should ask himself how he is initiating his children into manhood.

4. Fathers can be *mentors*. Mentoring continues the process by which a young man grows and matures. As a mentor the father teaches the boy how to be a productive member of the community and society. The mentor provides advice, sponsorship, and guidance.

5. Fathers can be *elders*. The older father can teach the boy-turned-man the wisdom learned through the ages. This wisdom involves a shift from the outside to the inside, from the physical to the spiritual, and from egocentricity to community-centeredness.

Exercise I: What kind of father are you?

It is important for us to take an inventory of our role as a father up until now, whether our children are young or old, male or female. Answer the following questions in your journal:

1. In what ways were (are) you involved in your children's birth?
2. Do you feel you matter(ed) to your children? In what ways?
3. When your children were born, what kind of father did you want to be? Have you been that kind of father to them?
4. How much alone time do (did) your spend with your children?
5. What rituals did (do) you have with your kids?
6. What was (is) your policy on physical punishment of your children?
7. In what ways are you a domineering father?
8. Are you sensitive to gender-related issues with your children? Do you and your spouse communicate at cross-purposes with your children? Do you draw the kids in as allies in family arguments?

Exercise II: The father you long to be

What kind of father do you long to be? In your journal answer the following:

1. Describe the qualities of the father you long to be (emotional, physical,

social, and spiritual).

2. What is your reaction to the following lessons you might pass on to your children?

- How to win and how to lose with dignity and how to play the games of life without always having to win; how to be a team player
- How to be with women and other men
- How to surrender, to be spiritual, to pray how to guide, teach, and lead
- How to commit to something, such as how to love and accept love
- How to like oneself, to be appropriately proud of oneself; how to respect self, others, the environment; how to deal with one's feelings
- How to touch appropriately; how to value one's own body
- How to care, to have hope, and to help others with wisdom
- How to find and use power respectfully
- How to value work appropriately, to have a vocation as well as avocation
- How to laugh, cry, think, follow through with whatever has to be done, and how to end things in a careful, caring manner

This inventory has described the father you are, have been, or long to be, as you perceive yourself. The next step is to ask yourself these questions:

1. How do you live out these values with your children? How do you make your "father love" accessible to your children?

2. What kind of father do you now want to be to your children?

3. How can you add more time with your children, regardless of what age they may be?

4. What spiritual wisdom have you learned so far in your life that you want to pass on to your children?

5. How can you find the time and opportunities to pass this spiritual wisdom on to them?

6. How can you be a wise elder to your children?

7. How has your addiction interfered with or affected your role as a father to your children? To children other than your own?

8 How can you now teach your children about self-possession, truthfulness,

responsibility, closure, and challenge? What do you want to say to them about these values, based on your own experiences so far in life?

9. What kind of help do you need to be the father you want to be?

10. What is your Achilles' heel as a father? Know yourself, admit it. What is it? Your temper, impatience, arrogance, or ignorance about children, adolescents, or young adults?

Exercise III: Action steps you can take

Next, it is time to act. How can you take the following steps with your children? Write down the action(s) you are prepared to take now to change your relationship with your children.

Step 1. The first step is to review your time commitments with your children. Despite all of the changing images of fatherhood discussed above, even today you may return home long after your infant children are in bed. Even if your sons are still awake when you come home, you may close yourself off by tuning into TV, alcohol, or other numbing behaviors. You may take business trips away from the family for days and weeks at a time. What are you willing to change in this regard?

You may work overtime or work two jobs to make ends meet. One day you wake up and the children have cars and are away from the home in the evenings and weekends. Then the kids get jobs or go to college. Nature seems to play a mean trick on you: the years when your children are growing are your most financially productive years. These are the years of ascent. Yet, by the time you realize that this lifestyle is taking a toll on you and your family, it is often too late. Your children are teens and have active lives of their own or do not desire to spend time with their "boring parents." A "family vacation" with teenagers is an oxymoron. The time of healthy family vacations may be over before it begins for you and your family. You may realize you have spent all of these years doing what you were told to do to win your father's and family's respect, but in the process have lost precious time with your children and spouse. It is time you can never fully reclaim. You may feel a void as you realize that, while dedicating your life to a successful career and being a good provider for your family, you have missed out on the deeper, more rewarding aspects of your life and parenting.

What do you need to do today to find time in your life for your children? What activities would they enjoy doing with you? What would you like to do with them? Is it time to change your priorities in life, to reorganize your life to become the father you long to be?

Step 2. Is it time for you to do something spiritually refreshing with your children? Perhaps you need to offer refreshing spiritual experiences to your children and yourself. You cannot give much to your children when you are running on empty.

Here are some hints to refresh your spiritual life with your children:

- Find a faith community or spiritual activity that you and your children can share. What would work for you and your children?
- Share spiritually-oriented books with your children. This can be as simple as reading stories from books such as *Chicken Soup for the Soul* to more profound spiritual writing. Share the poetry of Hafiz or Rumi. Read Annie Dillard or Annie Lamont, who speak of their lives' journeys. Read books with your sons like Richard Rohr's *The Wildman's Journey*. What would you and your children enjoy reading together?
- Go for a walk together in nature. Talk about nature's wonders, the mysteries of creation, the sounds of silence one finds in the forest or mountains, the sense of awe and wonder nature brings. Talk about your prior experiences in nature, your spiritual yearning for something greater than yourself, your sense of majesty when confronted by the magnitude of creation. How can you make this happen in your life as a parent?
- Talk with your children, especially as they are teenagers or older, about your own experience of powerlessness and the wounds and hurts in your life. Be vulnerable with your children. What can you do today to begin the conversation anew with your children?
- What activities do you really enjoy that you could share with your children, such as hiking, biking, fishing, or skiing? Maybe these were shared in the past but haven't been for some time. Which could you begin to engage in today?

Step 3. Spend time with other fathers. Talk about the fathers they long to be. You will learn you are not alone on this journey. With what other men in your life can you share your interests and concerns as a father?

Exercise IV: Write an ethical will

A useful exercise for many men is to write an Ethical Will to their children. Much as a man would write a will of his goods and possessions, a man can write a will that reflects the ethical, moral, and spiritual teachings and principles he wishes to leave them. Here is an exercise that asks you to write an ethical will to your children, regardless of their ages.

1. What would you leave behind in the hearts and minds of each of your children?

2. Would you leave different principles for your son(s) than your daughter(s)?

3. What lessons have you learned in life that you'd like your children to know?

4. You need not give the Ethical Will to your children at this time. That depends on their ages. If they are teenagers or adults you may wish to sit down with each of them and go over what you wrote in your Ethical Will.

Section 2:

TREATMENT METHODS

CHAPTER TWELVE
The Importance of Gender-Specific Treatment

For most male substance abuse clients, being in an all-male, homogeneous group presents some distinct advantages that are not available in mixed gender groups. All-male groups offer familiar terrain at a time when a man may feel particularly isolated and excluded. Although men often function in the public sphere, surrounded by work associates, and often report a large number of "buddies" or casual friends, men, particularly substance-dependent men, live lives of marked emotional isolation. Brehm (1985) found that men tend to have friendships characterized by "activity sharing" (e.g., hunting, working on a car, playing cards), whereas women are more likely to have friendships characterized by interpersonal intimacy and disclosure of feelings. Men prefer "side-by-side" relationships, whereas women prefer "face-to-face" relationships. Because men lead these emotionally isolated lives, many men may find that therapy groups offer immense potential for interpersonal communication and connectedness and recognition of common struggles. Yalom (1970) spoke of the importance of universality in groups, the awareness that we are all in the same boat together.

Furthermore, male-specific groups aid in overcoming male over-dependence on women to talk for them, as was the case with Chris in Chapter 3. Because men limit emotional expressiveness and intimacy with other men, they tend to become emotionally over-dependent on women. Men grant women expressive power, whereby men have learned to experience their emotions vicariously through women, and masculinity-validating power, whereby women confirm a man's worth through appreciation of his contributions as a protector, provider, or sexual gratifier. Because men have allowed themselves to become so dependent on women for social facilitation, nurturance, and validation, the all-male therapy group offers a valuable corrective emotional experience, as men learn together to trust and value intimate male friendships.

Male groups encourage participative self-disclosure. Men are traditionally wary of personal revelations, feeling that private admissions could cause them to be seen in a negative light. Individual counseling further exacerbates this inhibition given the power differential between client and therapist, especially if the counselor is a woman. The all-male group provides a potent environment to counter this antitherapeutic pattern so common among men in individual therapy.

All-male groups instill hope through listening to the testimonies of other men. This is some of the power of 12-step groups as men have a chance to listen to other personal stories and can find expectancy and hope in those stories. They provide a major source of incentive and demystification for men who might otherwise see counseling as a threatening or emasculating process. Groups further aid in the discovery of emotional connections. Although men can share deep and intense feelings and are capable of interpersonal connections, they typically interact intensely only when fighting or competing. Strong emotions expressed by one group member generate considerable affective resonance in other men, heightening the intensity of the change process. Many men in groups are amazed to realize the strength of the feelings they have suppressed.

Finally, groups aid in improving male communication skills. Farrell (1986) and Tannen (1990) noted a tendency of men to practice "self-listening," whereby a man listens to a conversation, not to take in or genuinely appreciate what a man is saying, but only to be able to jump in and discuss his own experiences. Men engage in "report talk," not "rapport talk." The group, as a social microcosm, is abundant with opportunities for men to experience the consequences of their communication style. When encouraged to experiment with alternatives, men can become far more effective in the interpersonal realm.

In sum, because male socialization emphasizes independence, emotional stoicism, and maintaining the upper hand in relationships, male resistance to counseling should be anticipated, understood, and respected. An effective tool for dealing with this socialization process is group work, which can propel men into a therapy journey that will profoundly alter their lives.

The 70/70% rule: A female-dominated profession.

The Center for Substance Abuse Treatment (2003) conducted a study of who provides treatment in the addictions field. The following are the results of this study:

- Approximately 70% of the clients in addiction treatment programs in America are men
- Although the majority of management personnel in treatment programs are men, 57-60% of the counselors in addiction treatment programs are women; this figure increases when traditionally female-dominant professions such as nurses, aids, educators, social workers, and social service workers are included
- 70% of new counselors entering the addictions field are female
- Why are these professions female-dominated? The issue is in part about money. The average salary for an addiction counselor in America in 2006 was in the mid-$30,000s. The salary range for a full-time counselor was from $27,000-$42,000
- More women are entering the field later in life as a second career after they have raised their children

These data raise profound questions about how addiction treatment is delivered in America, especially for men. If the majority of the patients are male and the majority of the caregivers are female, there may be a need to address the specific issues of men in treatment. This means that:

- Gender-sensitive treatment for men and women is needed. Chris's first counselor apparently was not male-sensitive. Research indicates that men, when placed in mixed gender groups, tend to be more task-oriented (as opposed to process-oriented) than the female group members. Men in mixed groups are less verbal and, when they do speak, are more cerebral and cognitive than women. Allowing the women in the group to "carry" the group emotions, they either placate or pander to the female members.

- Generally, men do better in male-led counseling, in male-only groups, as do women in female-led counseling and female-only groups.

Anecdotal research indicates that men form bonds with other men faster in male-specific groups, are more self-disclosing, and sense a greater kinship and brotherhood with other men when women are not present. Women seem to feel more able and open in discussing trauma and sexuality in female-specific groups;

- Counselors need gender-oriented training. The addiction counseling profession will not remedy the gender imbalance in treatment until salaries are on a par with similar professions and society's attitude about men in care-giving positions changes. Therefore, given the fact that the preponderance of counselors in the field will likely, for some time, remain female, we must address how to best work with men.

Women as Clinicians in All-Male Settings

In some respects female clinicians do play a beneficial role for male clients. Research indicates that men report matters about their family of origin more readily to female counselors than to male counselors (Webber, 1991). Men are generally more comfortable with women counselors when discussing affective issues. For their part, female counselors tend to be process-oriented rather than task-oriented. This is advantageous for some men, who otherwise might readily avoid dealing with their emotions by remaining task-oriented in therapy (Webber, 1991).

There are, on the other hand, some problems for women working as clinicians in all-male settings. First, some men may see their male counselors (if there are any in the agency) as the "real therapists," having the "real power" in the organization. Some men have difficulty "hearing" their female counselors, which likely has to do with differences between how men and women communicate (Gilligan, 1992). Some men may not be accustomed to communicating openly with women. Moreover, a female counselor cannot provide a positive male role model for a male client simply because she is not a man.

There may be a clash of styles between female clinicians and male clinicians or clients. "Masculine" is often thought to suggest "didactic, scientific, detached, non-committal" qualities. "Feminine" may be thought to mean "collaborative, non-competitive, nurturing." This stereotyping of behavior can be destructive to the therapeutic process. In addition, female clinicians may have different management styles from male clinicians (Rosener, 1990).

Some male clients may view the nurturing offered by a female clinician as "smothering." Female clinicians can project their own antagonism toward men onto their male clients.

Attachment theory holds that a female clinician working in an all-male setting can generate significant negative transference in the client as well as negative counter-transference in the clinician (Alderfer, 1991). Bob had a counselor assigned to him by an alcoholism treatment program. The counselor is divorced and harbors her own anger toward male clients who remind her of her abusive ex-husband. Bob is the current recipient of her negative counter-transference. Unfortunately, Bob experiences negative transference toward the counselor, too, as he sees her as a replica of his wife, who had been verbally abusive throughout their twenty-year marriage.

Men as Clinicians in All-Male Settings

There are several advantages of male clinicians working in all-male settings. Some well-known treatment centers, such as the Hanley Center and the Betty Ford Center, place men in all-male groups with male counselors only, and women in all-female groups with female counselors only. It has been the experience of these programs that all-male groups with only male counselors (and vice versa for the female clients) are a more effective way of structuring treatment.

Men tend to address tasks more readily with male counselors. This predisposition may work more effectively in a treatment setting that utilizes brief, task-oriented therapy models involving solution-focused and motivational interviewing techniques. Men view their male counselors as more legitimate than their female counselors, thus giving the male clinician a greater sense of empowerment. Men seem to understand other men more easily than women do. In addition, men will disclose some information to male counselors more readily than they will to female counselors (Webber, 1991; Alderfer, 1991)

At the same time, there are problems that can ensue from employing men as clinicians in all-male settings. Some male clinicians may reinforce negative male communication patterns, such as referring to women in derogatory terms. Men from racial and cultural groups that have been traditionally disempowered by society may find it difficult to conceive of letting go of their power in keeping with the 12-Step concept of powerlessness. Perceiving themselves as having little power in society, they feel a need to retain whatever limited power they think they have. An example of this is the homeless man who has used his survival skills as his only form of power. To be asked to give up this power to survive may be more difficult for the man to hear from a male than a female counselor.

Gay men may experience or fear more heterosexism in an all-male setting. Likewise, in an all-male setting (especially one not sensitive to the traditional male values of competition and dominance) some men may be more preoccupied with the racial, ethnic, and cultural issues that separate them from other men. Treatment staff, male or female, need to understand whatever biases men may bring to treatment.

Counseling Men: Structuring the Environment

Whether (or in what respects or circumstances) male or female clinicians are better suited to help male clients, clinicians and agencies must be sensitive to the impact of gender-related issues on patient treatment. This is especially true since (as noted above) female clinicians greatly outnumber male clinicians in a field that serves more male than female clients, Gender-specific clinical issues need to be addressed, both for men and for women. In particular, if men are to get help for their addictions, treatment must become more sensitive to male concerns.

There are a number of critical considerations in working with men. First, decision-making with respect to agency policies and procedures is aided when it reflects both male and female perspectives. Teamwork, co-facilitation of counseling, and collaborative working relationships between male and female staff benefit both the clinical team and the clients by providing positive role models for communication and cooperation between the genders.

It is imperative that the male voice be heard when the staff is predominantly female. Agencies need to take into account that men who are antagonistic toward women in power may have difficulty forming a healthy therapeutic alliance with female counselors. Not only are some men reluctant to disclose sensitive matters to female clinicians, but a female clinician may hold back her feelings in such a pairing as well. Rather than scapegoat or blame the patient or clinician for these problems, the agency needs to be sensitive to the impact of female staff on male clients and vice versa.

Likewise, gender and racial issues are rarely brought up by either supervisors or clinicians in supervision (Webber, 1991; Alderfer, 1991). It is essential, therefore, that the supervisor feel comfortable initiating the discussion of these issues with the clinician. It is the responsibility of both the clinician and supervisor to discuss sensitive issues that affect the quality of services offered to the client.

The critical questions of sexual attraction between clients and clinicians, dual relationships, and boundary violations are often raised in gender-specific groups, especially when there is a counselor of one gender treating a client of another. However, it is important to realize that sexual attraction and the risk of serious boundary violations occur in any gender configuration in clinical work. A number of sources provide useful guidance for clinicians and agencies concerning the wide range of ethical boundary dilemmas that arise in practice (Edelwich & Brodsky, 1991; Epstein, 1994; Gutheil & Brodsky, 2008; Reamer, 2001).

The structure of an all-male group is important. Men learn the rules of the game early, in the playground, on the ball field. Therefore, group norms and rules are critical for men. The explicit expectation is that all members be in place at group and ready to go when the group is scheduled to begin. Groups should also have some degree of structure, beginning with a check-in period and an arriving and gathering ritual, in which each man takes an uninterrupted turn to describe his week/day and to report on commitments made previously. A "jump ball" time is the period in which men begin the work of the group. Sessions should end with closing statements, an ending ritual, in which each member has a brief period to summarize his experiences of the session and to offer a behavioral commitment.

Group rules also need to emphasize confidentiality. It is essential, especially when working with men, to negotiate the limits of confidentiality within the boundaries of the duty to warn/protect. Counselors utilize standard techniques when negotiating these boundaries. In addition, group comfort standards are required as well as a model of accountability wherein the man is expected to make and keep his promises. There are also opportunities for humor and light-hearted emotional outburst, homework assignments, coaching periods, and "instant replay and slow motion" periods in which the counselor can stop the action for a process check. Other group procedures include role-playing behaviors, show-and-tell times when men can demonstrate their responses and actions, and therapist modeling and self-disclosure periods. Confrontations need to be customized to the needs and issues of each man, and positive behavior needs to be recognized and acknowledged. Male mentorship one to another is also important, as men are mimetic; that is, they have a tendency to model themselves after and to follow other men. It is more than an advertising slogan but a way of life for men to "want to be like Mike."

CHAPTER THIRTEEN
Overcoming Barriers for Men

Achieving coordinated treatment services for men is not an easy task, given the significant number of barriers to be overcome. In addition to the resistance and hesitancy of men to seek treatment in the first place, a number of environmental factors hinder the provision of appropriate care. The following is a list of some of these barriers:

- Uncoordinated treatment services; gaps in the availability of services.

- The need for better integration of treatment systems with other health-care and related systems, such as the criminal justice system, workplace systems (EAPs, human resource management programs), faith-based systems, government-sponsored systems, the military care delivery system, male-related organizations and systems, welfare-to-work systems, and family counseling systems.

- The lack of integration of residential/inpatient systems with outpatient systems. The weakest link in most inpatient treatment programs is the lack of coordinated, continuing aftercare programs. Most men are released from residential care with simply a copy of the Big Book, an AA referral, and perhaps a referral to an outpatient therapist for counseling. Yet experience indicates that a minimum of 6 months of aftercare is needed to maximize the gains of residential treatment.

- Social and system problems that impede treatment, such as political shifts in funding for services, politics (local, state, and federal), shifts in legislative and other public-policy priorities, and community attitudes about addiction, recovery, and men's issues. For example, a community may be far more receptive to offering services for women in recovery than for men, with a strong social stigma and prejudices against the male substance abuser. Community fears about potential violence and inappropriate sexual and other antisocial behavior all impede treatment.

- Mental health problems of alcoholic and drug-abusing clients. This includes the failure of many systems to diagnose co-occurring disorders (see discussion above about men and depression), related health-care concerns, aging and substance-abuse-related issues, and behavioral addictions (such as sex, gambling, and eating disorders).

- Difficulties in navigating the health-care and social-service systems. Among the causes of such difficulties are lack of education, medical or psychiatric complications, sexually-related disorders, developmental retardation, age-related difficulties, and chronic illness.

- Lack of financial resources or economic opportunities for men to get care.

- Male-based shame, stigma, and discrimination, including gender role stress (Efthim et al., 2001), a sense of physical inadequacy, emotional inexpressiveness, subordination to female caregivers, a sense of intellectual inferiority, or failure in meeting masculine standards of work and sexual adequacy.

- Stigma associated with cultural differences and sexual orientation, including societal homophobia and cultural biases against men seeking help, particularly in Latino cultures.

- Legal problems associated with recovery, including probation, incarceration, deportation, loss of child custody, lack of partner support, lack of support from family and friends, lack of transportation, language barriers, and other cultural issues.

- Lack of economic opportunities associated with involvement in criminal activities, gambling debts, prostitution, or violent crime.

The recovering man needs to be assisted in navigating treatment systems, particularly if the man lacks information or education on how to do so. The following factors have been found to affect retention of men in treatment: severity of addiction, involvement with the criminal justice system, employment issues, income, parenting responsibilities, and the therapeutic alliance.

Issues concerning mandated treatment also need to be addressed. Treatment practitioners should consider the following recommendations when designing programs for legally coerced clients:

- The period of intervention should be lengthy.

- Treatment programs should provide a high level of structure, particularly during the early stages of recovery.

- Programs must be flexible to meet the specific, unique needs of each male patient.

- Programs must undergo regular evaluation to determine their level of effectiveness and to detect changes in the client populations served (Hser and Anglin, 1991).

- Vocational training as an adjunct to care, especially for mandated clients with limited skills and employability.

- A careful review of stages of change and treatment readiness.

■ Development and consistent implementation of protocols for disclosure of information, especially sensitive information that might affect the patient's future recovery, employability, return to society, and parental and familial roles.

In addition, organizations need to make a commitment to male involvement, asking men to be included and advertising the agency's desire for male involvement in program literature, mission statements, and so forth. Agency staff should "put out the welcome mat" for men, engaging men in informal, positive conversation, showing empathy for men, and putting themselves in men's shoes in a variety of situations.

Agencies should display positive images of men in brochures, waiting-room magazines, on special occasions such as Father's Day, and in posters and artwork that depict men in a positive manner. Agencies should find out what men want by asking what they are feeling or thinking at the time and how they feel they can be helpful to themselves and others. They should ask fathers about their relationship with their children. Clinical staff should notice what men are doing and how they spend their time. It can be helpful to take a survey to find out what men might want from the program.

Agencies need to address staff attitudes, including resistance about dealing with men, that negatively affect men's treatment. They should conduct training and discussions with staff, using the following kinds of statements and questions: "We do not have many men involved in our program. Why not?" Or: "We could involve more men if...." Supervisors need to conduct an environmental audit of their program to determine how to implement services for men. This can be done by bringing in a panel of men to discuss men's issues and concerns with staff.

Agencies need to address resistance to men on the part of female staff by asking women about their relationships with their own fathers and significant men in their lives. Supervisors need to emphasize that children need both fathers and mothers and that all men have the potential to be responsible partners. Male or female bashing among staff should not be condoned, of course, and appropriate boundaries need to be established.

Agencies need to incorporate more men into the program by seeking out and hiring male staff and recruiting male volunteers. Men need to be incorporated into all aspects of the program, not just those geared to men's issues. Men will feel more comfortable in a setting where they see other men working and participating in activities.

Clinicians need to be aware of the characteristics of male group behavior. Supervisors need to inform counselors that "these are the things men do." Training and clinical supervision can be effectively utilized to increase clinicians' awareness of these patterns (Powell, 2004).

CHAPTER FOURTEEN
Screening and Assessment

When treatment professionals consider issues of screening and assessment of men with chemical dependency problems, they must be aware of the ways in which male gender influences the help-seeking behavior of men. In general, male gender role socialization contributes to a tendency for men to deny, misperceive, and minimize their need for assistance, particularly when that assistance is for biological, medical, or behavioral problems. For some men, seeking out a professional helper threatens their sense of masculinity. Since men are taught to ignore physical and psychic pain, they may see their distress as an inability to manage their problems themselves. It may imply low self-esteem, a sense of incompetence, a perceived loss of autonomy, or a fear of dependence on others for help (Addis and Mahalik, 2003).

As with most health care problems, men tend to seek treatment later in the addictive process than their female counterparts. Even when they do seek help, men may do so only in response to some external pressure and may deny or minimize the severity of the issue. Given this reluctance to seek assistance, it is important that health care professionals maximize whatever opportunity they have to fully evaluate a man's condition and to engage him in a helping relationship. Given that the quality of the therapeutic alliance has been found to be the single most important predictor of treatment outcome, the rapid establishment of a therapeutic relationship with a male client cannot be over-emphasized.

What can be done to engage a man in the screening and assessment process?

- From the beginning, clinicians can be sensitive to the influence of traditional male gender role norms on the screening and assessment process. Although men may share common attitudes and behavioral dispositions based on gender role socialization, there will also be some variability in personal definitions of and attitudes toward masculinity. Hence, the clinician needs to be attuned to these subtle variants in male gender role norms.

- Because men are generally ambivalent about seeking help for behavioral health problems, it is useful for the clinician to understand, as much as possible, what set of circumstances prompted a man's help-seeking behavior. Perhaps the most important question a counselor can ever ask a male client is "Why are you here? Why now? For help for what problem? And how can I help you?

- The stages of motivation for change illuminate all forms of treatment and are especially helpful when addressing male issues in treatment (Miller and Rollnick, 2002). Given that most men are brought up in a way that discourages seeking help for personal issues, clinicians working with chemically dependent men should expect to find ambivalence toward change along with possible resistance in the face of external pressure or coercion.

- When beginning the screening process, the counselor should conceptualize the engagement process as a series of steps in which the male client can move from stage to stage, from screening to treatment to continuing care. Men are goal-oriented. The primary goal of each clinical contact should be to ensure that the client will return for his next appointment. One step at a time. That is, even if treatment is clearly indicated, the counselor may first want to elicit agreement to do an initial screening to determine whether further assessment, followed by treatment, is warranted and acceptable to the client.

- Because men typically are action- and task-oriented, it is useful to emphasize the immediate goal of each step, from screening to assessment to treatment to continuing care. Each stage of treatment should come with a clear plan for what will happen and what the next steps might be. Tangible results should be part of this plan and contract. A letter documenting the visit, attendance, or phone call is helpful to provide tangible evidence of movement for the client. Giving the client something to do to prepare for the next session can facilitate engagement and support the man's sense of confidence, control, and efficacy. It will also emphasize the collaborative nature of treatment, emphasizing the client's freedom of choice. Generally men seek autonomy, so a man should be offered the ability to decide what process he wishes to follow.

- Similarly, it may be useful to acknowledge explicitly the difficulty men have seeking assistance. If the client expresses the concern that his need for treatment is a sign of failure or weakness, it may be useful to reframe such comments by defining help-seeking behavior as a sign of strength and courage in the face of traditional gender role stereotypes.

- There are also specific techniques clinicians should use during the initial screening sessions with a man. Because men may be particularly uncomfortable with emotional expression early in the process, the counselor should carefully monitor the emotional intensity of initial interactions, offering men time to compose themselves if needed. In some cases it may be useful to defer exploration of feelings until there is less anxiety about the helping process and a better working alliance. Clinicians should also carefully monitor the interpersonal intensity of initial interactions. Again, it can be helpful to avoid competitive exchanges, comments, or questions that might provoke shame. To decrease the potentially uncomfortable intensity of close contact with a counselor (especially if she is a woman), it may help to sit with the man at an angle or side-by-side rather than directly face-to-face. During clinical assessment, men may prefer more physical distance between the clinician and the client. In some settings, talking while walking and other strategies that decrease the intensity of direct eye contact may help the man feel more comfortable.

- Eco-maps, genograms, family maps, timelines, concept maps, mode-link maps, and graphs of scores on screening and assessment measures can be used to create the kind of concrete, visual representations with which some men are more comfortable working (Halpern, 1989).

Finally,

- Clinicians must acknowledge that substance-abusing men can be aggressive, often commit property crimes, and may present in a state of acute intoxication. As a result, when men are seen for abuse assessment, the physical setting and clinical procedures must allow for effective management of aggressive behavior, prevention of theft (particularly if cash or medications are kept on the site), and effective management of acute intoxication. Although some women come for care in an intoxicated state as well, men are more commonly seen in emergency rooms and crisis intervention centers in a state of acute intoxication.

For further information on conducting a comprehensive assessment of substance-abusing men, the reader is referred to TIP 24, *A Guide to Substance Abuse Services for Primary Care Physicians* (CSAT 1997). In summary, there are three steps in a comprehensive substance abuse assessment:

1. The screening phase
2. The problem assessment phase
3. The personal assessment phase.

In the problem assessment phase, gender-sensitive personal assessment is pursued. This includes consideration of psychosocial adaptation, substance use patterns, and help-seeking behavior of men. The assessment also should be sensitive to ways in which age, ethnicity, socioeconomic status, geographic location, and sexual orientation contribute to differences in values, attitudes, and behavioral dispositions to substance use and abuse. That is, while considering ways men are alike because of their gender, clinicians must also be sensitive to ways in which men differ from one another.

Standardized assessment approaches are available. Retrospective methods using timelines and follow-back procedures define the nature and consequences of substance use during a specified period of time. Again, because men tend to be more comfortable analyzing visual information (Halpern, 1997), visual presentation of substance use and consequences of use along a timeline or on a calendar may be a more gender-sensitive manner to collect and display the information to a male client. Prospective methods using calendars or other means of personal record-keeping can document patterns and consequences of use. Laboratory studies are also used in screening to document recent use, obtain markers of chronic use, and document medical consequences of chronic use. Although they are effective with women as well, these concrete measurements play to men's propensity to problem-solving and visual representations.

For the personal assessment phase of the comprehensive assessment, standardized instruments such as the Addiction Severity Index (Mathias, 1994) are often used for historical and concurrent problem assessment. It is important to distinguish between confirmatory and compensatory drinking and drug use for men. Confirmatory drinking styles involve using alcohol because it is consistent with personal definitions of masculinity that men have integrated into their definitions of self. Compensatory drinking styles involve using alcohol to shore up a tenuous sense of one's self as a man or to deal with stress associated with perceived failure to meet traditional male gender role expectations (Williams and Ricciardelli, 1999). Other male-sensitive instruments are the Male Role Norm Scale (Thompson and Pleck, 1986), the Gender Role Conflict Scale (O'Neil, 1995), and the Masculine Gender Role Stress Scale (Eisler, 1995). Other, longer instruments that are male-sensitive are the Brannon Masculinity Scale (Brannon and Juni, 1984) and the Male Role Norms Inventory (Levant et al., 1992).

Because there are clear links between poor physical health and both male gender and chronic substance abuse, any comprehensive substance abuse assessment must include a complete physical examination. Ideally, the exam will include lab studies to screen both for health problems associated with the use of specific drugs and for health problems more generally associated with men. If the male client is being seen in a hospital or residential setting, a complete physical exam with lab studies should always be part of the routine admission process. In ambulatory settings, the initial interview should include questions about health history, general nutrition, sleep patterns, weight changes, last physical examination, and last dental examination. In addition, when feasible, a full personality assessment is beneficial, including the following areas:

- Antisocial personality assessment and mental health status
- Assessment of motivational levels
- Assessment of family history
- Assessment of childhood and other trauma
- Assessment of criminality, anger, and physical violence history
- Assessment of sexual functioning
- Risk-taking assessment
- Assessment of personal relationships, educational history, vocational background, leisure activities, and spirituality/religious background and orientation.

To get to some of the more sensitive issues, such as shame, the interview might include reflections such as "You feel ashamed about _____. Can you describe what that's like? How often do you sense that, feel that way?" Responses to these short questions can be used to quantify the frequency and intensity of reactions such as shame, guilt, and anxiety. The Internalized Shame Scale (Cook, 2000) is an exceptional tool for assessment of male clients.

CHAPTER FIFTEEN
Clinical Approaches to Treating Men

The clinician needs to assist male clients in developing communication skills; in differentiating among being assertive, passive and aggressive; and in learning how to say no (refusal skills). Some male clients may need to learn how to take "no" for an answer. The counselor may need to talk about and model how to treat women with respect and to give women power to consent without intimidation. Some male clients may need to learn listening and conflict resolution skills, especially to begin with the words "I feel" or "I am" when expressing an emotion.

Non-violent role models need to be offered to male clients, encouraging empathy and being able to talk about feelings. Counselors can teach men fathering skills, including affirming, caring, nurturing, forgiving, patience, and vulnerability. Non-stereotypical male activities such as art, poetry, music, and community service should be supported by the agency. Non-traditional professions such as nursing, administration, and early childhood education should be encouraged. Clinicians need to honor non-violent sports that foster cooperation, bonding, and commitment, while affirming new, less competitive sports activities as alternatives to the traditional male preoccupation with competition and violent sports. Agencies need to combat homophobia among their staff and in their community. Clients need to be encouraged to discuss how sexual violence has affected them and other men and ask what part they can play in the solution to violence.

Joe has a history of violence at home, occasionally beating his wife and children. He has difficulty with anger management and impulse control. For years Joe has been in and out of addiction treatment programs that never addressed his anger. Each time, upon discharge, he'd return to the same pattern, using alcohol as a tool so that he could vent his anger. Finally Joe finds a treatment program that addresses his anger. As part of this treatment for his addiction the counselors teach Joe how to control his temper, how to find other, non-violent forms of release, and how to communicate calmly with his family. After a year of group counseling, Joe is clean and sober and his family life is significantly improved.

In an age of heightened awareness of cultural, racial, and gender issues, it is important for clinicians working with substance-abusing and dependent men to know the concerns of specific subpopulations and cultures. Economic circumstances and their related social and psychological problems introduce a common set of challenges and tend to create a lower quality of life for many people, especially people of color (Johnson et al., 1995). Low socio-economic status is the most prominent common factor in the lives of many African-Americans, Hispanics, Asian-Americans, and American Indians. Low levels of education, underemployment, and lack of health insurance, resulting in limited access to health care and consequent exacerbation of health problems, are generally associated with lower socio-economic status and higher substance abuse rates.

The first step in treating men is to acknowledge cultural issues and develop greater cultural competency with men. Bell (1985) and others have written extensively about substance abuse and ethnicity. Further study is needed with respect to substance abuse and sexual orientation (including bisexuality), substance abuse and older men, geographic subcultures (such as rural vs. urban lifestyles for men as well as inner-city behavior), and substance abuse in the context of physical disabilities. Further, drug-specific treatment components are necessary to address the full range of behaviors of substance-abusing men. Finally, relapse prevention strategies specific to men need to be designed.

Motivational Enhancement with Men

Motivation is considered a major aspect of personal change and growth.

Motivation is multifaceted and constantly fluctuating along many dimensions. It is commonly observed by health care providers that men are very difficult to get into treatment for any health-related problem, especially substance abuse, and that motivation for care is a critical factor in involving men in treatment. Men seem to require different levels of motivational engagement that depend not only on the substances used and their consequences, but also on the degree to which men believe in and support values that are consistent with our traditional concepts of what it means to behave like a man (Addis and Mahalik, 2001; Blazina and Watkins, 1996).

These values and perceptions are not fixed, but do in fact constantly change to some extent as we go through life. One obvious challenge is to motivate men to overcome some of these commonly accepted male attributes that deter men from seeking help for their alcohol and/or drug abuse problems. One way to enhance this motivation is to change the structure and strategies of the treatment program to be more responsive to the habits and psychosocial needs of the men served. Some programmatic recommendations along these lines are discussed above.

Men often complain they feel as if they are treated like children by caregivers as well as educators. This decreases their motivation to follow through with treatment, especially in inpatient settings. Men's socialization around power seeking, control, and self-reliance works against motivation for treatment. Perhaps the challenge for substance abuse treatment providers has more to do with changing our societal views and assumptions about men and manhood than with treatment itself. Enhancing treatment motivation has to start before a man comes to a health care provider, if in fact it is more likely that he will never show up than that he will present himself voluntarily.

External motivation (for example, a failed marriage, a court order, loss of a job, or an EAP referral) may force someone to seek help before he elects to do so on his own initiative. Media attention to male attitudes about health care and help-seeking also can provide some form of external motivation. However, changing how men are socialized will probably yield more positive results than anything we can do programmatically. By encouraging more conducive attitudes regarding emotionality and help-seeking behavior, we can create the opportunity to change this pattern of self-perceived weakness.

The utilization of Motivational Interviewing (MI) as a means to create relationship and help each man find his own intrinsic motivation is highly recommended. Skilled use of MI can have a positive effect on behavioral change (Miller and Rollnick, 2002).

Twelve Step Programs

The issues particularly relevant for men in recovery that 12 step programs typically address include the following: a sense of isolation and loneliness; power and powerlessness; trauma and crisis; judgment, comparing, contrasting, and competing; sponsorship and mentoring with other men; and spirituality. These are areas in which 12 step programs are particularly helpful for men, providing a safe and accepting environment where men can address these issues. Closed meetings for men are useful in opening men up to such issues, in ways they might not otherwise feel safe or comfortable doing. Therefore, we highly recommend a program of 12 step recovery as a component of men's treatment, when chemical dependency or another behavioral/process dependency (sex, gambling, food) is present. Such programs provide an environment and meeting place that is rarely found or available to men except in faith communities. Just think about it: where else do men meet except in bars or sporting events, all of which center around drinking, drugging, or competition?

Outpatient vs. Residential Services

For some men, such as the homeless or men suffering from more severe addictions and co-occurring disorders, special considerations are needed with respect to the location and type of treatment. Consideration needs to be given to the man's housing status, employment capabilities, detoxification and medical status, and potential recovery resources. The American Society of Addiction Medicine Patient Placement Criteria (PPC-2) are most helpful in finding the right placement level for patients (Mee-Lee, 2005). As men have higher rates of criminal behavior, homelessness, and medical complications than women, these need to be factored into finding or making the proper patient placement.

Numerous studies have been done on the efficacy of outpatient vs. inpatient treatment (Miller and Hester, 1980; Miller et al., 2003). However, there is a paucity of studies on patient placement when applied to the treatment needs of men specifically. Although residential treatment had been the modality of choice for quite some time, reductions in funding have made residential care ("28-day treatment") no longer the "gold standard" for rehabilitation. However, in the light of newly recognized male-specific concerns, researchers may need to revisit the efficacy of outpatient services for particular men dealing with such issues.

Other potential components to be considered in designing a continuum of services for men are shelters, transitional living arrangements, half-way and quarter-way housing, emergency seasonal housing/shelters, and domiciliary arrangements.

Individual Counseling

The NIDA Individual Counseling Model outlines strategies for counseling on a one-on-one basis (Washton, 1990; Mercer and Woody, 1992; NIDA Therapy Manuals). The key question is that of the advantages and contraindications of individual counseling for men. It may be easier for some men to engage in individual counseling because they do not have to deal with their gender-related image and interpersonal issues in front of a group of people. For some men, it will be much easier to discuss sensitive issues and deal with emotions and tears in privacy with a trained professional than it would be with a group of peers whom he will face again after admitting to and/or revealing aspects of himself that he normally would not share with other men. Although the group is bound to confidentiality, a professional enjoys a different level of trust from the client's perspective, especially given legal and ethical constraints. Also, the counselor is not seen as a peer or potential friend, but as someone providing a service in a context-specific relationship that is very personal, but very circumscribed in time, setting, and purpose (Gutheil & Brodsky, 2008).

Some research indicates that men engage in one-on-one treatment with a male therapist more effectively than with a female therapist (CSAT TIP on Treating Men, in development). Nonetheless, the NIDA manual points out that, given all of the issues of control and power that men have (O'Neil, 1982), in male client-male therapist interactions clients must be respected and have equal power in determining the outcome of the relationship. They must be allowed to maintain their dignity and self-respect while allowing another man to help them on an emotional and behavioral level. Even the most client-centered male counselor may be seen by a male client as someone who is better than or superior to him. It is important, therefore, that the counselor establish an environment where there is no power dynamic or negative judgment on his part. Rather, although he and the client have different roles in the relationship, they have to work together with mutual respect if the alliance is to be successful.

In regard to the female counselor in individual sessions with a male client, several issues are worth considering.

- The nature of the mother-son relationship experienced by the client will greatly affect the client's ability to work with a female counselor.

- It may be helpful for the female counselor to explore the male client's feelings about being in a therapeutic relationship with a woman. The negative attitudes some men harbor toward women may intentionally or unintentionally lead to hostility, sometimes expressed in aggressive behavior, that will impede the therapeutic process.

- Although the focus of the counseling is on substance use and abuse, it may be helpful for the female counselor to explore the nature of the client's relationship with his parents, given that the relationship between a man and his parents can shape how the man views and relates to women. Relationships with wives, girlfriends, lovers, sisters, and other female figures are worthy of attention as well.

- The focus is not to just understand how the client feels about women, but also to give him the opportunity to get in touch with his feelings about women and about having a female counselor.

Family Intervention

Family work has a long history in the substance abuse treatment field. However, family-oriented interventions pursued with men must be sensitive to the effects of gender role socialization on the client and his family life. The following areas need to be addressed:

- Enhancing the client's ability to think about the influence of gender role socialization on the presenting problem.

- Promoting the idea of shared responsibility for change in the relationship.

- Actively challenging stereotypical attitudes and behaviors.

- Family-oriented engagement: promoting self-care for family members, decreasing the risks of domestic violence, promoting communication between the substance-abusing individual and his partner, and reinforcing the client's and family's efforts to function on a daily basis.

- Marital intervention to promote an atmosphere of abstinence, mutual respect, and open and healthy communication between partners.

- Parenting intervention: fathering roles, child-care responsibilities, the male partner's responsibility for sexual reproduction, problematic attitudes about parenting, socially responsible parenting, healing father-child breaches, overcoming long-standing generational parenting issues (including family-of-origin issues), legal barriers to effective parenting, improving the relationship with mothers (who typically control access to children), improved communication skills with children, specific parenting skills, overcoming family secrets about substance abuse and related behaviors, and aiding the substance-abusing father in providing emotional support to children.

- Addressing violence issues, including domestic violence or child abuse and neglect perpetrated against or by the alcoholic/drug abuser.

- Legal assistance with family court matters, including divorce, child custody, child support, allegations of abuse or neglect, child welfare and family court systems, and societal stereotypes of substance-abusing men as indifferent, uninvolved, irresponsible, and irrelevant.

- Reproductive responsibility, unwanted paternity, intimacy disorders, communication patterns, gender stereotyping, sexual misconceptions, and social pressures associated with sex roles and gender. Programs should also address sexual health, risky sexual behaviors, and pregnancy-related questions.

Counseling Strategies

Be aware of the male socialization process and the conditioning that goes with it. Have a vision of the person underneath the conditioning (innate characteristics and capacities), and offer that vision and awareness to the male client. For example, show you know the man is good/, caring, likable, or capable even if his actions or the way he displays his distress does not remind you of these qualities.

Don't view men as merely the effects of their conditioning and react reflexively. Rather, acknowledge the conditioning and speak to the inherent person. The way men display their conditioning is a road map to the hurt they have endured. The distress-laden ways in which men at times act, for instance, often reflect either how they were treated or how they learned to act to cope with the way they were treated.

Realize that because of narrowly defined expectations and their inability to recover from hurt, men often lose track of very basic needs. These needs get channeled in other, often inappropriate ways.

Look for the real needs that lie underneath the appearance. For example, often men's longing for sex is really a longing for caring, with no other accepted avenue to feel it. Men's violence is often an expression of feeling out of control and uncontained. Their real need is for structure and for experiencing control of one's internal environment.

Learn to help men face the feelings that lie underneath their attachments to people, objects, sensations, and experiences. Some examples might include:

Women............affection, softness, other "feminine qualities"

Children...........play, pride, ownership

Cars...............freedom, control

Work...............self-worth
Competition.........self-worth, a place in the world
Alcohol............relief, freedom from stress (of course, alcoholism will take on a control of its own)

Often, when men get "stuck" on something, it represents an effort to meet a real need. However, this effort to meet the need becomes rigid (frozen need), and the person falsely equates the attachment to the person (or whatever) with the meeting of the need.

Don't expect men to understand or readily accept your attempts to assist them in working through their socialization. Men's attachments to their coping styles are as deep as they needed to be to survive the conditioning process. Men will cling to those strategies until it is clearly safe to let go.

Don't attack men for these struggles. Men struggle as a result of persistent attacks they have coped with. Hold them accountable for their effect on others, but if you want change, offer a hand.

In offering a man a way out of conditioned styles of coping, you will often uncover and encounter the feelings (anger, rage, loneliness, desperation) that were swallowed when he initially succumbed to the conditioning. Expect these feelings and help the man process the feelings and behave appropriately.

Help men not only face but release their feelings. Many men show sensitivity to feelings, but have major barriers to releasing them.

Use positive, socially accepted male language to encourage and support men as they look at themselves.

"It's brave of you to share your feelings."

"It will be helpful to others, too, if you face these issues."

"There is much more ahead for you if we look at this...."

Honor the other ways men have been able to cope with situations or manage their emotions.

Help men live with ambiguity. The male training is to be decisive, opinionated.

Be aware of your own re-stimulation. All of us, men and women alike, have been hurt by rigid "male" patterns of control and distorted "power." Stay out of your own victimization. Working on re-stimulation alone will take concerted effort and will pay off in more relaxed attention to male clients.

Counseling with a man has a tremendous potential power due to the intimacy that may be experienced by the male client. Most men have not been offered much closeness in their lives. A counseling experience may give him a remarkably higher quality of one-to-one attention than he has ever experienced. Respect this, pace things well, and use this opportunity.

Sexual feelings may come up in the counseling experience. Most men have had feelings of shame heaped on their sexual feelings and consequently remain secretive in these areas. Offer safety. If it is safe for you, allow the possibility that the client may experience sexual feelings in relation to you as a male or female therapist. There are specific techniques that can help work on these feelings, but acknowledging them may be a good start.

Male counselors may need to help the male client deal with homophobia in the relationship as it arises. This necessitates that you as counselor examine your own possible internalized homophobia.

Perhaps above all, if you can offer men a bridge to the neglected parts of themselves you will give them a tremendous antidote to their socialization.

Section 3:

TREATMENT RESOURCES

CHAPTER SIXTEEN
Homework

What's the simplest way to make a good counseling session even better? Give the client a homework assignment. Just how powerful are homework assignments? One homework assignment literally altered the face of treatment.

In an interview shortly before his death, Albert Ellis, the father of Rational Emotive Behavior Therapy (REBT), told the interviewer a fascinating story about a landmark psychotherapeutic homework assignment he gave himself that spawned the REBT movement and changed the course of counseling and therapy for at least the next fifty years.

At age 19, Ellis was petrified at the thought of approaching women. Two hundred days a year he would go to the Bronx Botanical Garden in New York wanting to meet women but not having the courage to initiate conversation. Ellis began reading the work of the early behaviorists suggesting that if you confronted your fears they would often disappear. So, in the words of Albert Ellis, "I gave myself a famous homework assignment in August" (Rosenthal, 2002).

Each day he challenged himself to approach every single woman who was alone on a park bench and talk to her. "I'll give myself one minute, one lousy minute," he told himself, "and if I die ... well ... I die." He approached more than one hundred women. Thirty immediately got up and walked away (not too bad considering Ellis did his homework assignment in New York City, not known for its friendliness to strangers). Out of all the women only one made a date with him and she subsequently didn't show up. The good news was that Ellis overcame his fear of approaching women. From that point on, homework became one of the bedrocks of his theory.

William Glasser, the father of reality therapy, wrote, "Psychotherapy can begin in the office, but it must be lived outside of the office. Homework with therapy is a good way to get this process started" (Rosenthal, 2001).

What type of therapist uses homework assignments? A better question might be: What type of therapist doesn't? In fact, psychotherapeutic homework is used by individual therapists, group therapists, and marriage and family counselors. In addition to rational emotive therapy and reality therapy, counselors practicing assertiveness training, behavior therapy, cognitive behavior therapy, conditioned reflex therapy, gestalt therapy, career counseling, neuro-linguistic programming, transactional analysis, person-centered therapy, brief-strategic or solution-oriented therapy, and logotherapy, to name a few, use homework assignments in their counseling practices. In sum, outstanding therapists from virtually every therapeutic orientation give their patients homework assignments.

Homework assignments take advantage of the fact that most people are actually very adept at modeling the behavior of others, as well as anticipating what others will say or do. The use of homework allows the patient to progress at a faster rate and flourish as if they were receiving additional sessions (something we can all use in the age of managed care). Another plus when working with an alcohol or drug abuse client is that homework assignments zero in on one of a substance abuser's worst hurdles: What to do when an uncontrollable urge to engage in an addictive behavior occurs outside the treatment setting.

Homework assignments may not be appropriate for the first session or two. Literature has shown that the counselor should meet with the client a minimum of three or four sessions before prescribing homework assignments (Rosenthal, 2002). We do not necessarily agree with this assessment, for we have had good success--with men in particular--using homework assignments early in the therapeutic relationship.

Also, the counselor should always tailor the assignment to the client's specific problem (e.g., drinking, drugs, love addiction, etc.). One way to introduce the exercise to the client is to say, "I have noticed that you are an extremely perceptive person. For instance, you seem to know exactly what your boss is going to say. In the last session you suggested that your brother would call you and ask you to go drinking on Monday night and he did. I have seen you for nine sessions now and you probably have an excellent idea of what I'm going to say and how I'm going to say it. So here's what I want you to do, if you are willing [it is important here to get permission for the upcoming directive]. Whenever you get the uncontrollable urge to drink (gamble, etc.) I want you to begin a dialogue as if you were right here in my office. In other words, based on what you have learned in our sessions, I want you to tell me about your urges and then play the part of me and respond to yourself. If you are not sure what I would say, just take an educated guess. You can write it in a journal or record the imaginary session into a tape recorder. Bring your journal or your tape to the next session so we can examine it."

In many cases the mere act of creating the make-believe session curbs the client's urge to engage in the addictive behavior. The beauty of this simple exercise is that it teaches the client to think like a counselor, which is one of the most important goals of treatment or rehabilitation.

Finally, the counselor should challenge herself to create her own innovative homework assignments. The following are recommendations to help the counselor develop her own materials and assignments:

- Use only assignments with which the counselor feels comfortable.

- Carry out the strategy in a spirit of empathy and optimism.

- Always check ethical guidelines prior to implementing any technique.

- Use caution to ensure that clients are not embarrassed or physically harmed by the assignment.

- If the counselor is new to the field or undergoing close supervision for licensure or certification, he should check with his clinical supervisor before he prescribes a homework assignment to be certain it fits within the therapeutic model of the agency at which he is working.

- Role-play the homework assignment with a trained colleague or supervisor before attempting it for the first time with a client.

- Never attempt a technique for which the counselor has no training or clinical supervision.

- Do not assume that even an effective homework assignment will work in every case.

- Do not assume that a homework assignment that worked well with a client will work effectively with the same client at a later date.

- Always take multicultural and diversity considerations into account.

- Use only language the client can understand. Be as specific as possible.

- Bend, fold, and mutilate existing strategies to increase the counselor's comfort level and to meet the needs of the client.

- Realize that some homework assignments need to be used repeatedly to be effective.

- Realize that therapeutic timing can make or break a technique.

When giving homework assignments there are clear guidelines to follow:
- Provide a clear rationale for the homework assignment, linked to the client's mutually agreed upon treatment goals.

- Make the homework relevant to the focus of the counseling sessions.

CHAPTER SEVENTEEN
Bibliotherapy

Most people realize how therapeutic reading can be. When we read we enter the world described in the pages of a book and become involved with the characters in the story. When we read a good book, we often close the book having gained new insight and ideas. This is the purpose of bibliotherapy: to assist a client in overcoming the emotional turmoil related to a real-life problem by having him/her read literature on that topic. The story read can serve as a springboard for discussion in counseling and possible resolution of the dilemma. The therapist can offer guidance in the resolution of personal issues through the use of directed readings and follow-up activities.

The client is appropriate for bibliotherapy after they go through three stages or tests:

Identification - the client is able to identify with a book character and events in the story, either real or fictitious. Sometimes it is best to have a character of approximately the client's age facing similar events.

Catharsis - the client is able to become emotionally involved in the story and can work to release pent-up emotions in counseling.

Insight - the client, after catharsis (with the help of the counselor), can become aware that their problems might also be addressed or solved. Possible solutions to the book character's and one's own personal problems are identified.

Bibliotherapy can be conducted in individual, family, or group therapy. In individual bibliotherapy, literature is assigned to a client for a specific need. The client may read the material or the literature may be read to him. The activities that follow the reading are also conducted individually with the client. After discussing the literature with his therapist, the client can be asked to do homework by talking his responses into a tape recorder, writing them down in journal, or expressing them artistically. Through this process the client is able to unblock destructive emotions and relieve emotional pressures.

Additionally, by examination and analysis of moral values and the stimulation of critical thinking, the client can develop greater self-awareness, an enhanced self-concept, and improved personal and social judgment. This outcome should result in improved behavior, an ability to handle and understand important life issues, and increased empathy, tolerance, respect, and acceptance of others, all through identification with an appropriate literary model.

When bibliotherapy is used with groups, the patients read literature out loud or listen while the counselor reads to them. Group discussion and activities follow. Clients become aware that they are not alone in their feelings and that their perceived problems are shared by others.

Although bibliotherapy encourages change within the individual, its use is not restricted to crisis situations. However, it is not a cure-all for deeply rooted psychological problems either. Some deep-seated issues may best be resolved through more intensive therapeutic interventions. Some clients, not yet able to view themselves in a literary mirror, may use literature for escape only. Others may tend to rationalize their problems away rather than face them. Still others may not be able to transfer insights into real life. Nonetheless, guided vicarious experiences with literary characters prove to be helpful for many patients.

How To Use Bibliotherapy

1. First, the therapist should identify the client's needs. This task is done through observation, counseling sessions, and review of the client's records.

2. Match the client with appropriate materials. The therapist should find books that deal with the presenting issue: divorce, a death in the family, or whatever needs have been identified, keeping the following in mind:

   a. The book must be at the client's reading level.

b. The book must be at an interest level appropriate to the maturity of the patient.

c. The theme of the readings should match the identified needs of the patient.

d. The characters should be believable so that the client can empathize with their predicaments.

e. The plot of the story should be realistic and involve creativity in problem solving.

3. Decide on the setting and time for the bibliotherapy assignment and how the patient will be introduced to the literature.

4. Design follow-up activities for the reading (e.g., discussion, paper writing, drawing, drama).

5. Motivate the client with introductory activities (e.g., asking questions to get a discussion going on the topic).

6. If the reading is to be conducted in the presence of the therapist, the therapist should engage in the reading, viewing, or listening phase. Ask leading questions and start short discussions throughout the reading. Periodically, summarize what has occurred thus far (to be sure that "the message" does not get lost in the details).

7. Take a break or allow time for the client to reflect on the material.

8. Introduce some or all of these follow-up activities:

-Retelling of the story

-In-depth discussion of the reading (e.g., discussing right and wrong, morals, the law, strong and weak points of the main character, etc.)

-Art activities (e.g., drawing map illustrating story events, creating collage from magazine photos and headlines to illustrate events in the story, drawing pictures of events)

-Creative writing (e.g., resolving the story in a different way, analyzing decisions of characters)

-Drama (e.g., role playing, reconstructing story with puppets made during art activity, enacting a trial for the characters)

9. Assist the patient in achieving closure through discussion and a listing of possible solutions, or some other activity.

Cautions

- Avoid topics (e.g., abortion, drug use, crime) that might draw concerns from the patient or family members, unless approved by the patient and concerned parties.

- The therapist should be familiar with the book. He should read and understand it before using it.

- The therapist should write a precise set of homework instructions for the client in clear, understandable language.

In an age when self-help books fill sections of bookstores, when individuals often search these shelves or the Internet for help with problems, bibliotherapy may have reached a new high in utility to clients.

Bibliotherapy has been used in clinical practice for decades. There are several valuable texts and research studies that discuss the use of homework and bibliotherapy in counseling. The recommended text for this section is J.M. Joshua and D. DiMenna's Read Two Books and Let's Talk New Week (2000).

There are many benefits to homework assignments and bibliotherapy:

- To help clinicians track clinical progress and modify treatment (Beitman, 1987)
- To enable clients to practice what they have learned in therapy (Budman, 1988)
- To maximize the effects of therapy on the client's world and environment (Bandura, 1969)
- To advance progress so as to lead to greater self-reliance beyond the therapeutic hour (Haley, 1973)
- To serve as a bridge between the client's therapy and real life.
- To increase the client's awareness of their issues
- To increase emotional regulation and catharsis, bringing feelings to light through the use of the printed page
- To increase interpersonal effectiveness by reading about individuals who have overcome adversity and resolved their issues

- To overcome obstacles by finding solutions in the lives and accomplishments of others.

The following is a bibliography of books recommended for assignment to clients, based on the client's diagnosis or presenting problem. It is not an exhaustive list. For further information on these books or other recommended texts for bibliotherapy, the reader is referred to the text by Tompkins, Using Homework in Psychotherapy (2004), and to Michael Gurian's user-friendly book, What Stories Does My Son Need (2000).

Domestic Violence

He Promised He'd Stop, M. Groetsch
When Men Batter Women, N. Jacobsen and J. Gottman
The Courage to Heal, E. Bass and L. Davis
Secret Survivors, E.S. Blume
The Sexual Healing Journey, W. Maltz
Victims No More, M. Lew

Verbal Abuse

Tongue Fu, S. Horn
The Verbally Abuse Relationship, P. Evans
You Can't Say that to Me!, S.H. Elgin

Addiction & Recovery

The Addictive Personality, C. Nakken
Children of Alcoholism, J.S. Seixas and G. Youcha
My Mama's Waltz, E. Agnew and S. Robideaux
Perfect Daughters, R.J. Ackerman
A Ghost in the Closet, D. Mitchel
I'll Quit Tomorrow, V. Johnson
I Wish Daddy Didn't Drink So Much, J. Vigna
Recovery: Plain and Simple, J. Lee

Other Addictions
Codependent No More, M. Beattie
Out of the Shadows, P. Carnes
Addiction & Grace, J. May
Cocaine Addiction, A.M. Washton

Adoption
Being Adopted, D. Brodzinsky & M. D. Schechter
The Primal Wound, N. Verrier
Shadow Mothers: Adoption & Reunion, L. McKay
Let's Talk about it: Adoption, F. Rogers

Anger
The Anger Workbook, L. Bilodeau
Angry All the Time, R. Potter-Efron
The Angry Teen, W.L. Carter
The Dance of Anger, H. Lerner
Facing the Fire: Experiencing and Expressing Anger Appropriately, J. Lee
The Missing Peace: Solving the Anger Problem for Alcoholics, Addicts, and Those Who Love Them, J. Lee
Men's Work, P. Kivel

Chronic Illness
Alzheimer Sourcebook for Caregivers, Gray-Davidson
Coping with Alzheimer's, R.E. Markin
Cancer as a Turning Point, L. LeShan
Conquering Pain, R.S. Prust and S. Luzader
Facing & Fighting Fatigue, B.H. Natelson
The AIDS Dictionary, S.B.Watstein and K. Chandler

Divorce
Can this Marriage Be Saved? M.D. Rosen
The Healing Journey through Divorce, P. Rich
At Daddy's on Saturday, L. Girard and J. Friedman

Divorced but Still My Parents, S. Thomas
Do I Have a Daddy? J.W. Lindsay and C. Boeller
Helping Children Cope with Divorce, E. Teyber
Mom's House, Dad's House, I. Ricci
Essential Grandparent's Guide to Divorce, L. Carson
Exorcising your Ex, E. Kuster

Gay, Transgender Issues

Bi Any Other Name, L. Hutchins and L. Kaahumanu
Lesbian & Gay Parenting Handbook, A. Martin
The Journey Out, R. Pollack and Cheryl Schwartz
Finding the Boyfriend Within, B. Gooch
Intimacy between Men, J. Driggs and S. Finn
Coming out of Shame, G. Kaufman and L. Raphael
Coming out Spiritually, C. de la Huerta
Like Bread on the Seder Plate, R. Alpert
The Other Side of the Closet: The Coming-Out Crisis for Straight Spouses, A.P. Buxton
When Husband Comes out of the Closet, J. Gochros
Trans Liberation, L. Feinberg
True Selves: Understanding Transsexualism, M. Brown

Grief & Loss Concerns

Grieving, T. Ranks
Giving Sorrow Words, C. Lightner
Healing Journey through Grief, P. Rich
Necessary Losses, J. Viorst
Saying Goodbye to Daddy, J. Vigna
When Dinosaurs Die, L.K. Brown and M. Brown
No Time for Goodbyes, J. Lord
The Grieving Child, H. Fitzgerald
A Broken Heart Still Beats: When your Child Dies, A. McCracken and M. Semel
How to Survive the Loss of a Child, C. Sanders
On Children & Death, E. Kubler-Ross

How to Survive the Loss of a Parent, L. Akner
Longing for Dad, B. Erickson
Losing a Parent, A. Kennedy
Motherless Daughters, H. Edleman
When Parents Die, E. Myers
Companion through the Darkness, S. Erickson
How to Survive the Loss of a Love, M. Colgrove
Living with Loss, E.S. Stern
Widow to Widow, G.D. Ginsburg
When Men Grieve, E. Levang

Suicide

Straight Talk about Death for Teens, E. Grollman
Why Suicide? E. Marcus

Alternative Medicine

Healing and the Mind, B. Moyers
Healing Words: The Power of Prayer, L. Dossey
Healthy Aging, A. Weil
The Natural Mind, A. Weil

Medications

Listening to Prozac, P. Kramer
Beyond Ritalin, S.W. Garber and M.D. Garber
Straight Talk about Psychiatric Medications for Kids, T.E. Wilens

Mood Disorders

Anxiety Cure: An 8 Step Program, R. Dupont
If You Think you Have Panic Disorder, R. Granet
Moodswings, R.R. Fieve
The Childhood Depression Sourcebook, J. Miller
Winter Blues, N. Rosenthal
Growing up Sad, L. Cytryn and D. McKnew
Breaking the Patterns of Depression, M. Yapko

Depression, D. Rowe
On the Edge of Darkness, K. Cronkite
Undoing Depression, R. O'Connor
I Don't Want to Talk About It: Overcoming the Secret Legacy of Male Depression, T. Real

Obsessive-Compulsive Disorders

Passing for Normal, A.S. Wilensky
Stop Obsessing! E.B. Foa and R. Wilson
Tormenting Thoughts, I. Osborn

Schizophrenia

Is There No Place on Earth for Me? S. Sheehan
The Quiet Room: A Journey Out of the Torment of Madness, L. Schiller and A. Bennett
Schizophrenia: the Facts, M.T. Tsuang

Money

Everything you Know about Money is Wrong, K. Ramsey
Financial Peace, D. Ramsey
Overcoming Overspending, O. Mellan

Parenting/Families

Bradshaw on the Family, J. Bradshaw
Good Enough Mothers, M.M. Marshall
How to Talk so Kids will Listen, A. Faber
The Mother Dance, H. Lerner
The New Peoplemaking, V. Satir
Parents Do Make A Difference, M. Borda
P.E.T., T. Gordon
7 Habits of Highly Effective Families, S. Covey
Touchpoints, T.B. Brazelton

Attention Deficit Disorders and Other Behavior Problems

The Broken Cord: FAS, M. Dorris

Driven to Distraction, E.M. Hallowell

How to Handle a Hard to Handle Kid, C. Edwards

Your Kid has ADHD, Now What? J. Schaub

Positive Parenting Your Teens, K. Joslin

Real Boys, W. Pollack

Men's Issues

The Flying Boy: Healing the Wounded Man, J. Lee

Fire in the Belly, S. Keen

Iron John, R. Bly

Playing Life's Second Half: From Success to Significance, D. Powell

The Irritable Male Syndrome, J. Diamond

Stiffed, S.Faludi

The Myth of Male Power, Warren Farrell

Male Menopause, J. Diamond

Step-Parenting and Single-Parenting

Blending Families, E.F. Shimberg Family Rules, J. Lofas

Parenting Keys, C.E. Pickhardt

The Second Time Around, L.J. Janda

The Single Father, A.A. Brott

Difficult Relationships

The Angry Marriage, B. Maslin

Emotional Unavailability, B. Collins

He's Scared She's Scared, S. Canter and J. Sokol

Too Good to Leave, Too Bad to Stay, M. Kirshenbaum

After the Affair, J.A. Spring

Surviving an Affair, W. Harley & J.H. Chalmers

Intimacy & Sexuality

The Future of Love, D.R. Kingma

Couple Sexual Awareness, B. McCarthy
Is there Sex after Kids? E. Kriedman
Passionate Marriage, D. Schnarch
The Soul of Sex, T. Moore

Spirituality

Awaken to Your Spiritual Self, M.J. Abadie
Treasuring the Treasure: Exploring Spirituality, R.M. Beshara
Conversations with God, N.D. Walsh
A Course in Miracles, Foundation for Peace
Going to Pieces without Falling Apart, M. Epstein
Expect a Miracle, D. Wakefield
The Road Less Traveled, M.S. Peck
A Return to Love, M. Williamson
The Seat of the Soul, G. Zukav
The 7 Spiritual Laws of Success, D. Chopra
The Spirituality of Imperfection, E. Kurtz
Tuesdays with Morrie, M. Albom
Working with Emotional Intelligence, D. Goleman

Creativity, Work, Stress at Work

People, S. Covey
Real Power, J.A. Autry and S. Mitchell
The Web of Inclusion, S. Helgesen
Crossing the Unknown Sea, D. Whyte
Creating a Life Worth Living, C. Lloyd
No More Blue Mondays, R. Sheerer
7 Habits of Highly Effective People, S. Covey
Beat Stress Together, W.M. Sotile
Chained to the Desk, A Guidebook for Workaholics, B. Robinson
Dealing with People You Can't Stand, R. Brickman

Activities and Discussion Questions

The therapist should locate various books, stories, and film-clips or videos that deal with personal problems. He should then decide if the materials are appropriate for bibliotherapy, listing for his use the whys and why nots of the literature. If a book is deemed appropriate, the counselor should decide which ages, groups, or types of patients would be the target population for these materials. Once the materials have been located and identified, the counselor should devise introductory and follow-up activities for the books or other literature recommended.

CHAPTER EIGHTEEN
Video Work

Video work is an extension of bibliotherapy, a tool in therapy. Today, men and women like to watch movies and do video work more than they do reading. We seem to be more visual than ever. Films are fun, require small amounts of time and money, fit into the average man's busy routine, and enable him to readily identify with dilemmas of those portrayed in film and to easily recall plots and characters. Film acts as a therapeutic metaphor, providing the male client with a visual portrayal of something they might be feeling or living with. Finally, video work is time-effective and efficient, saving both the client and the counselor undue time spent in accessing feelings. In a time when outcome and efficiency greatly influence what happens in counseling, video work addresses concerns of time, money, and results.

Further advantages of video work include:

- Videos and film combine realism with imagination, allowing the male client, when viewing a video, to create his own reality or to illustrate the reality in which he is living;
- Men like to watch films. Therefore, recommending a film to a male client and having him view the movie is generally a pleasant part of treatment;
- Films overcome language barriers since most DVDs today have subtitles in various languages;
- For those who are homebound and may not be able to go to a theatre or may not have a social life due to their geographic confinement, VHS tapes and DVD's viewed at home provide an avenue to growth and learning;

- Movies and films can be shared with family and friends, allowing for dialogue and exchange, especially for men who might not be part of the counseling program or are unwilling to participate in therapy; given many men's reluctance to seek help, film therapy is a good "foot in the door to counseling";
- Films enhance rapport building and the deepening of the therapeutic alliance between the counselor and the client;
- Movies often are in the client's vernacular, taking the application out of the psychobabble of the counseling room and putting the discussion in the common language of most men; and,
- Films and the media raise a level of curiosity for most clients, encouraging change and growth through "benign" interventions.

Films and movies aid in treatment planning in at least seven ways:

1. They offer hope and encouragement to clients, such as the release illustrated in *Shawshank Redemption*.

2. They provide an opportunity to reframe the problem, as in *Starting Over*.

3. They provide positive male role models for success and significance, as in *Rudy*.

4. They offer a means of identifying and reinforcing the client's internal strengths, as portrayed in Parenthood and *The River Runs Through It*.

5. They dramatize emotions, as in *The Son's Room* and *This Boy's Life*.

6. They aid in improving communication between men and their partners or family members, as shown in *Accidental Tourist*.

7. They aid in prioritizing values, meaning, and purpose, as in the challenging and troubling movie *Short Cuts*.

There are significant differences between viewing films for *entertainment* purposes and for *therapeutic* value. In films used for entertainment the focus is on plot; action is essential to the experience; content and outcome are central; and there is a spirit of excitement. When films are used therapeutically the characters and relationships become central; the emphasis is on process, not content. The purpose of viewing for therapeutic benefit is to gain insight into oneself and one's life in relation to the characters portrayed.

When doing video work with men, the therapist treats the film and characters as co-counselors, aiding in the therapeutic process and relationship. The purpose of video work is to augment, not replace, therapy. The goal of video work is not to analyze the film, but to gain personal insights. Neither the client nor the counselor is a film critic.

Furthermore, the counselor should genuinely enjoy viewing movies. It is critical that the therapist try it before he buys it. Unless the therapist has a bottomless wallet, it is far less expensive to go to the local video store and rent the film before investing $15-20 in purchasing it.

The counselor should "test drive" a film before recommending it to clients. This involves viewing the film and thinking about how it addresses a problem from your past or present experience. It is helpful to test drive the film by inviting a colleague, friend, or family member to view and discuss the film with you, noting the characters with whom all parties identify. What emotions and insights are demonstrated? Pretend that a client saw the film. What questions or issues would the client have about the film? How can the film be used in video work with men? What clients might appropriately view this film? For what clients, clinical diagnoses, or presenting problems would this film not be appropriate?

The range of subjects covered in films is enormous. Here is a simple sampling of topical areas for which films can be used in therapy with men:

- Parenting, marriage, intimacy
- Communication
- Illness, trauma
- Loss, grief, depression
- Irrational fears, anxiety
- Family-of-origin issues
- Substance abuse
- Physical abuse, domestic violence, child abuse
- Divorce and custody
- Eating disorders
- Gender issues
- Identity, vocation
- Spirituality

■ Death and dying

The following section is a listing of films and media that can be used in therapy, organized by topic and diagnostic category. As it is not the goal of this manual to provide a detailed analysis of each film and how it can be used in therapy, the reader is referred to Hesley and Hesley's *Rent Two Films and Let's Talk in the Morning* (2001) and Solomon's *Reel Therapy* (2001)

For general inspiration, the following movies are recommended: *On Golden Pond, A River Runs Thru It, Pay it Forward, Rudy, Field of Dreams, Billy Elliott, Shawshank Redemption, It's a Wonderful Life, Strangers in Good Company, Shadowlands, Tender Mercies, About Schmidt, Million Dollar Baby, Tuesdays with Morrie, Babette's Feast, The Trip to Bountiful, Apollo 13,* and *Patch Adams.*

A current all-time favorite movie about life, meaning, the purpose of existence, and quantum physics (now there's a combination) is *What the Bleep Do We Know.* Not exactly romantic evening viewing, but certainly a thought-provoking and stimulating film that should engender significant discussion. There is now even a study guide available on this film with questions and discussion points. Check it out at Amazon.com or your local bookstore.

The following movies are excellent for portraying how support can be found from a number of sources, such as family, friends, colleagues, and assorted others who come in and out of our lives: *The Big Chill, Circle of Friends, City Slickers, Fried Green Tomatoes, Steel Magnolias, The House of D,* and *Peter's Friends.*

On the subject of men and women's search for meaning and significance in life, the following films are highly recommended: *American Beauty, The Apostle, Being There, Cider House Rules, Dead Poets Society, Short Cuts, Field of Dreams, It's A Wonderful Life, Jonathan Livingston Seagull, My Dinner with Andre,* and *The Truman Show.*

There are many films demonstrating men's personal courage, without having to dip into the Rambo genre. Movies that portray courage, conviction, strength of character, commitment, and concern for others include the following: *Chariots of Fire, Master and Commander, Field of Dreams, The Pianist, Gandhi, Life is Beautiful, Shawshank Redemption,* and *Forrest Gump.*

Clinicians need to be critical and careful in the use of video work in therapy.

Not every man is a suitable candidate for video work. Men with serious psychopathology or severe symptomatology are not candidates for film work; neither are young boys. When there is violence in the home that might be reignited by a graphic film, video work is not recommended. For clients who have experienced recent trauma, films are potentially risky as they might provide too real a portrayal of life issues.

Conversely, not all films are recommended for clients. Movies with graphic images, vulgarity, blatant sexuality, excessive violence, or antisocial behavior are also unlikely candidates for video work. Such films include *Trainspotting, Clockwork Orange, Pulp Fiction,* and many war movies, such as *Apocalypse Now, The Deer Hunter, Saving Private Ryan* (the scene at the beginning with the invasion at Normandy in World War II), and *Hanoi Hilton.* For veterans, especially those of the Vietnam era, such films might promote flashbacks and dissociation. When working with men who have experienced the traumas of combat, the therapist needs to be very selective in the choice of films.

The following are tips for selecting films:

- Select films that provide effective role models.
- Choose films that evoke inspirational moods.
- Match the content of the film to the therapeutic issues and the client's lifestyles and values.
- Select films that show characters solving problems.
- Take advantage of powerful indirect effects of films, such as portrayal of positive familial and social relationships and productive lifestyles.
- Pick films that men enjoy.

When assigning films to men, think how a film strikes you when you view it. Here again, men working with men should view the film and see it through a man's eyes. What is the central issue of the film? What did you find useful when you viewed the film? How did you feel when the film was over? Did you feel more depressed than before it began? Did you feel refreshed? Happy? Sad? What value might this film have for someone else? What male characters did you identify with? What characters might a male client identify with? How was this film similar to or different from your life? From the lives of your clients? What attributes would you like to take from what characters? What attributes would you like to avoid? Who are the protagonists/antagonists in the film? What obstacles were portrayed? What challenges were overcome, and how were they overcome? Were there traps and snares to be avoided?

It is helpful to list the adjectives describing the key film's characters and how they solved or did not solve their problems. Can you apply these adjectives to your life and that of your clients? How can this film help clients reach their goals? How can this movie solution work for your clients? Is the outcome realistic? Is it attainable and achievable?

Begin with films you've seen. What films do you like? Since we all have our favorite flicks, listen non-judgmentally to others' responses to films. For the first video work assignment with a client, choose a film that you prefer or something similar. Prior to viewing, discuss with the client whether there are any offensive aspects to the film (language, sexuality, nudity, violence, conflicts in values, etc.). If the client objects to viewing a recommended film do not pursue it. It is better to try another film. Before beginning the film, clarify for the client the intent of video work. Tell him that if he strongly dislikes the film he can turn it off. It is important for the client and therapist to admit to assignment mismatches quickly before any harm is done. Ask the client to look for films he thinks might be more therapeutically useful. Let him select the next film assigned.

It is important for the therapist to normalize the exercise, emphasizing the benefits of video work and explaining why a particular film was recommended. Describe the characters to be portrayed before viewing. Discuss possible problematic scenes and process how the client might feel when seeing those scenes. Assure the client that the exercise will be discussed at the next counseling session(s).

Ask the client to take notes when viewing the film. Give the client permission to stop the film when he has an insight, to replay important and moving parts of the film, and to discuss it with other men. The client should note the characters he likes or dislikes and explain why. Instruct him to write down the main points of the film that he wants to discuss in the next counseling session.

During the next session the counselor can explore with the client the questions raised above: How did the film strike him? What were its central issues? What did he find useful or unhelpful in the film? Of what value is this film to him, to someone else? What characters did he identify with and why? How was this film similar to his life? What attributes would he like to take from what characters? What to avoid? Who were the film's antagonists? What obstacles were overcome and challenges met, and how?

Occasionally, video work with clients fails for one of a number of reasons. When this occurs it is helpful to review the inaccurate interpretations the client might have had and why that occurred. Was there denial, aversion, or perceptual differences about the film between the client and the therapist? Did anything in the film violate a core value of the individual? It is helpful for the therapist to explore with the client the dissimilarities between his life experiences and those portrayed in the film. Finally, it is useful to ask the client to suggest another film that might work better for him.

Video work in training and supervising counselors.

Films also can be used in the training and clinical supervision of counselors. Most films that are suitable for treatment purposes work well for training as well. Therefore, rather than repeat the recommended films for clients and counselors, the next section will discuss films by category for treatment, training, and clinical supervision. Also, it will be obvious that some films are applicable to a variety of categories.

To start us off, the following is a list of films by diagnosis:

All that Jazz - Narcissism

As Good as it Gets - Obsessive Compulsive Behavior

David's Mother - Autism

Don Juan Demarco - Delusions

Falling Down - Antisocial Behavior

Fatal Attraction - Borderline Personality

Mr. And Mrs. Bridges - Depression

Mr. Jones - Bipolar Disorder

What About Bob? - Anxiety, Panic disorders

For addiction, substance abuse, alcohol and drug abuse and dependence, the counselor and/or client are recommended to view: *Clean and Sober, The Lost Weekend, Leaving Las Vegas, When a Man Loves a Woman, Days of Wine and Roses,*

Soft is the Heart of a Child (a wonderful, older film worthy of finding and adding to your agency's video library), and *Afflicted*.

There are several important films that explore issues of diversity, discrimination, affirmative action, cultural mores, sexism and racism, gender equality, and civil rights, including *A Star is Born, Joy Luck Club, Philadelphia, A Raisin in the Sun, My Family,* and *Rainman*.

Regarding marriage, children, divorce, parental custody, family therapy, and parent-child relationships the list is lengthy and rich, including films such as *Kramer vs. Kramer, Ordinary People, Little Man Tate, Rudy, The Secret Garden, American Beauty, Mrs. Doubtfire, The Great Santini, To Kill a Mockingbird, Life is Beautiful, Ma Vie en Rose, Mask, The Miracle Worker, Parenthood,* and *Searching for Bobby Fischer*.

Many men we see will confront family and parenting issues, including concerns related to single parenting, blended families, sibling relationships, adoption, custody of children, letting go, family conflicts, and the empty-nest syndrome. Films are an excellent tool when working through such life issues. In these areas the following films are recommended: *The Accidental Tourist, As Good as it Gets, Mrs. Doubtfire, Tender Mercies, Ulee's Gold, Step Mom, Fly Away Home, Hannah and her Sisters, Long Day's Journey into Night, Marvin's Room, On Golden Pond, Terms of Endearment, The Good Mother, Losing Isaiah, Breaking Away, Father of the Bride, Little Women,* and *A River Runs Through It*.

For video work in couples and communication counseling and when addressing issues related to commitment in relationships, the following are appropriate: *The Doctor, Erin Brockovich, The Horse Whisperer, He Said, She Said, The Four Seasons, Husbands and Wives, The Postman, Scenes from a Marriage, When a Man Loves a Woman, About Last Night, The Age of Innocence, Groundhog Day, High Fidelity, Nine Months, An Officer and a Gentleman,* and *The Story of Us*.

Films that address overcoming the pain and guilt of extramarital affairs, renewed intimacy, and dealing with divorce are: *Afterglow, Bridges of Madison County, Something to Talk About, Accidental Tourist, Pleasantville, Shakespeare in Love, Bye Bye Love, Kramer vs. Kramer, Starting Over,* and *War of the Roses*.

The last film, War of the Roses, is an excellent example of the need for the therapist to be sensitive to the film's content and to whom she recommends the film, as *War of the Roses* is filled with violent images of conflict, resulting in the eventual deaths of the principal couple (portrayed by Michael Douglas and

Kathleen Turner)-now we've ruined the story for you. So, choose wisely!

For films dealing with conflict and negotiation, abandonment, premature death of a child, and widowhood, we recommend *Message in a Bottle, Shadowlands, Places in the Heart, Who's Afraid of Virginia Woolf? Ordinary People, He Said, She Said,* and *Strangers in Good Company.*

There are unique issues related to aging, death and dying. The list of recommended films for these issues is extensive and rich, including *Cocoon, On Golden Pond, Space Cowboys, Strangers in Good Company, My Life, Shadowlands, Message in a Bottle, Ordinary People, A River Runs through It,* and *The Son's Room.*

When clients are working through various psychopathologies, it is often helpful for them to see a dramatization of those pathologies, such as anxiety disorders and obsessive compulsive behavior. Outstanding examples are the funny and charming movies *As Good as it Gets* and *What about Bob? The Great Santini* is a dramatic portrayal of family violence and controlling behavior. Other movies displaying psychopathology include *What's Eating Gilbert Grape, The Rain Man, Shine,* and *Ordinary People.* Suicide is dramatically seen in films such as *Dead Poets Society, Ordinary People, Whose Life is it Anyway? and What's Eating Gilbert Grape? Post Traumatic Stress Disorders* (PTSD), phobias, and eating disorders are shown in *Beloved, Saving Private Ryan, Fearless, Eating, The Truman Show, Vertigo,* and *La Vie en Rose.*

Some counselors address issues related to teamwork and vocational concerns. The following movies are recommended: *Clockwatchers, About Schmidt, Field of Dreams, Patch Adams, Erin Brockovich, Good Will Hunting, Apollo 13,* and, yes, even *Top Gun.*

Here are some specific films to view and how to use them in discussion:

Movies about men and their fathers: *City Slickers, Field of Dreams, The Great Santini, Swimming Upstream, Big Fish, Around the Bend*

Movies about men and their children: *Soft as the Heart of a Child, Ordinary People*

Movies about men and their addiction: *Basketball Diaries, Days of Wine and Roses, The Lost Weekend, Addict* (starring Johnny Depp, a film about methamphetamine abuse), *Spun* (also about methamphetamine addiction), *Born on the Fourth of July* (starring Tom Cruise as Ron Kovic), *Requiem for a Dream, Owning Mahoney* and the classic film *The Gambler* (films about gambling addiction), *Love Liza* (about sniffing gasoline), *When a Man loves a Woman* and *Drunks* (portrayals of the benefits of participating in A.A.), *Tender Mercies* (portrays someone in recovery from alcoholism), and Eugene O'Neill's *Long Day's Journey into Night* (an excellent portrayal of a woman addicted to morphine, played by Katherine Hepburn).

Films to avoid: *Arthur* (which glamorizes drinking and driving), *28 Days* (which set group therapy in addiction treatment back a decade), *Harvey* (where Jimmy Stewart plays a happy, comical drunk), *Up in Smoke* (which glamorizes drug use), *Easy Rider* (glorifying hallucinogens), *Ray* (again, although realistic, portrays a high-functioning Ray Charles on heroin).

When shown to professional staff, some films provide much fodder for ethical debate. *Final Analysis, Mr. Jones, The Butcher's Wife,* and *Prince of Tides* all show caregivers sexually involved with their clients. On the other hand, films such as *Antwone Fisher, Ordinary People,* and *Good Will Hunting* raise interesting questions and ethical challenges for counselors and supervisors to wrestle with.

Movies about men and work: *About Schmidt, Ikuru*

Movies about men and sexuality: *Something's Gotta Give*

Movies about men and spirituality: *Babettes Feast, Contact, The Doctor, Patch Adams*

To illustrate the use of film we have selected three movies to discuss, with sample questions to explore. This same process can be used with other movies.

City Slickers:

Healing themes: trying to find yourself, being stuck in a relationship, taking risks, father-son issues, commitment, effects of the past, parenting, friends and support.

Main lessons:

- Good friends are an asset in dealing with the ups and downs of life.
- Lasting relationships require a heavy dose of commitment.
- The remedy for burnout is to do one's job well and have varied interests.
- Fathering is about doing positive activities together as well as having long talks.
- Life is a series of "do-overs"-chances to try something once again and this time do it better.

Questions:

    1. What is the key message from the three friends regarding their fathers, and how would you relate these statements to your own father?

    2. What was the role of Curly in the lives of the three leading men?

    3. How did each of the men resolve their life changes and new approaches to life?

Field of Dreams:

Healing themes: father-son relationship, reconciliation with the past, following one's dreams, hearing the voices within.

Main lessons:

- Never stop dreaming, the spice of life.
- Support for a partner means taking his or her visions seriously even when they are not one's own.
- Set goals and stick with them. Don't give up.
- To forgive a parent, it is necessary to walk in his or her shoes.
- Burnout may be a symptom of dwelling on mistakes.
- Sometimes one has to act on information that is less than complete.
- To reach one's goals, help others reach their own.

Questions:

    1. What is the place where dreams come true for each of the characters?

    2. What reconciliation comes after the field is built? How will this give Ray greater peace?

    3. Why will people come to the field of dreams?

The Great Santini:

Healing themes: father-son relationship, alcohol abuse and its effects on the family, dominating personalities, masculine behavior, domestic violence, adolescent drinking.

Main lessons:

- Parents must protect their children from physical and emotional abuse.
- A spouse who is isolated needs a support system for reality testing.

- Fierceness and compassion can exist in a healthy mix.
- Assertiveness should be employed to break free from overbearing parents.
- Real men are strong enough to cry.

Questions:

1. When you saw the basketball scene, what feelings and emotions were generated? Could you relate the scene to your experience with your father? Other men?

2. What are your reflections on the role of alcohol abuse in the family?

3. How have you dealt with dominating men like Bull Meachum in the movie?

CHAPTER NINETEEN
Art as a Therapeutic Tool

Art therapy uses the creation or viewing of art to help people discover and express their feelings. Unlike art for art's sake, which focuses on the finished piece, art therapy (which typically employs paint, clay, charcoal, pastels, or other art materials) focuses on the process of creation itself. Moreover, the activity is undertaken primarily for its healing benefits rather than for the creative end result; in fact, the piece of artwork may never be shown to anyone outside the therapy session. Once an image has been placed onto a sheet of paper, molded from clay, or any of the other myriad ways that an image emerges, the creator then can relate to it and share its meaning with the therapist. That is therapy.

Art therapists believe that the act of making a piece of art triggers internal activity that contributes to physical, emotional, and spiritual healing. For people who are not able or ready to create art, going to an art museum or looking through art books can also be helpful. Simply viewing art refreshes the spirit and promotes relaxation.

While people have always expressed their feelings through art, art therapy as a profession has existed only since the 1930s. Among the fields that now frequently incorporate art therapy as part of the treatment process are clinical psychology (in which art is used to uncover hidden emotions) and physical therapy (which uses art to help build self-confidence and aid rehabilitation).

Child psychologists and family therapists often use art therapy because children have a hard time putting feelings into words. Art therapy has also become a vital part of the activities offered in many nursing homes, long-term-care facilities, and hospices.

How It Works

Art therapy helps healing in various ways. First, the aesthetic quality of the work produced can lift a person's mood, boost self-awareness, and improve self-esteem. Second, research shows that physiological functions, such as heart rate, blood pressure, and respiration, slow when people are deeply involved in an activity they enjoy. In addition, making art also provides an opportunity for someone to exercise their eyes and hands, improve eye-hand coordination, and stimulate neurological pathways from the brain to the hands.

Because art therapy uses a language other than words, it is often employed in treating patients with physical or emotional illnesses who have difficulty talking about their fears and hopes or about their anger and other strong emotions. The creation of art helps people get in touch with thoughts and feelings that are often hidden from the conscious mind.

Art therapy is not only the careful and ethical facilitation of art-based directives; it is also the concern and respect that is given to the image and the emotional well being of the maker. In regard to the respect that the image requires, an art therapist is careful not to interpret the meaning for the client as to not let the therapist's projection confuse or stifle the therapeutic value of the image. Some interpretation is inevitable, perhaps as a way to suggest general connections to previously mentioned material or to bridge the separation from awareness that the client may have about what they are now viewing. However, there are never any times to be absolute about interpretation.

Health Benefits

The mere act of creating art has intrinsic benefits, according to art therapists. By promoting feelings of achievement, the creation process automatically boosts self-esteem and self-confidence.

Stress reduction is also a significant benefit. Studies have shown that repressing strong feelings can lead to a buildup of stress and that stress can intensify pain as well as the symptoms of various diseases. Because art in therapy helps people access their unconscious mind and release pent-up emotions, it has been found to be very useful in treating those suffering from stress and stress-related ailments.

Art therapy is also used as treatment for behavioral problems and often serves as an ancillary treatment to psychotherapy. It is frequently part of inpatient psychological treatment programs, including those for drug and alcohol abuse. Patients recovering from trauma or serious injury often find art therapy particularly beneficial, as do people with chronic illnesses, such as Parkinson's or Alzheimer's disease. In addition to these uses, art therapy can also help people with a serious or terminal illness create a tangible record of their thoughts and emotions.

Art making also has a healing effect, merely through allowing opposite brain activity to occur. This bypassing of intellectualization allows for the expulsion of emotions, giving visual representation to otherwise silent energies. In our society, much has been discussed about the intelligence capacity of individuals; however, little has been discussed of the creative intelligence that everyone possesses. In treatment settings, this "intelligence" is often overlooked in favor of didactic and psychoeducational forms of treatment. When the decision is made to provide an intellectual framework for recovery or therapy, coupled with emotional and non-verbal targeting, a fuller and enhanced form of healing can be reached. Still, the slightest mark on a blank sheet of paper can be considered a creative expression. Therefore, the client who has engaged in making such a statement has participated in the therapeutic domain.

The use of art therapy-based modalities in addictions and other treatment settings appears to be on the rise. Brian Blocker, MA, LMHC, who was consulted for this chapter, has been employed in primary-addictions facilities as well as in those focused on aftercare and trauma, where art therapy was an integral part of the treatment team goals. In a treatment facility, art materials are generally stark and basic; however, a pencil or pen is generally all that is required. Brian's passion for art therapy still resounds at Hanley Center long after his return to his beloved New Mexico. Colorful collages, beautiful and poignant masks, and enormous group painting projects adorn the walls of the Center for Men's Recovery. Display cabinets in waiting areas offer glimpses in molded clay of a man's pain or pure joy.

Art therapy is not an "adjunctive" form of therapy, although it often is regarded and referred to as such. Art therapy should not be utilized except by a licensed art therapist. The American Art Therapy Association (AATA) has specific requirements that a facility must adhere to in order use the term "art therapy" or "art therapist." In order to practice art therapy, the practitioner must meet the qualifications AATA has set forth, which require education and training through a graduate-level program from an accredited school. One generally must also meet state or national qualifications for licensure in order to practice as an art therapist. Further information about art therapy and art therapists can be found through the AATA website or by contacting the art therapy chapter for your state.

CHAPTER TWENTY
Finding One's Inner, True Self:
That Other Thing, Poetry as Access to the Spirit

Whatever you do or imagine,
Begin it; be in your boldness.
Being in your power has beauty
And magic.... It is why you are
Here.... In Life.
Stephen Andrew

When working with men, remember the maxim: you sometimes have to hit them over the head with a hammer to get their attention, to get them to move from their left to right brains. One way of hitting men "over the head" is through poetry. The poet has a way of saying things that we mortals are unable to, what Emily Dickinson referred to when she described poetry as "that *other* thing." In Celtic mythology poetry is in the realm of "tien a' nog," which is translated as "just the other side," just behind the thin veil of words.

So, we have found poetry to be a vital source of inspiration for men. We highly recommend poetry by David Whyte, who seems to speak especially to the male soul, as does William Butler Yeats, among many others. David Whyte's *Crossing the Unknown Sea: Work as Pilgrimage is* recommended.

Here are a few of our favorite poems.
Leonard Cohen, *Anthem*
Leonard Cohen, *Hallelujah*

Robert Bly, *Snowbanks North of the House*
David Whyte, *Self-Portrait*
Blair Adcock, *Weathering*
David Whyte, *Sweet Ulysses*
David Whyte, *Revelations Must be Terrible*
David Whyte, *Enough*
David Whyte, *The Faces at Braga*
David Whyte, *The Half Turn of your Face* (see page **)
David Whyte, *The Journey*
Rainer Maria Rilke, *You Darkness*
Ralph Waldo Emerson, *Success*

There are many less famous but equally powerful poems specifically penned for and from the male perspective. Two of our favorite anthologies of such poems are *Men of Our Time: An Anthology of Male Poetry in Contemporary America,* edited by Fred Moramarco and Al Zolynas (1992), and *Rag and Bone Shop of the Heart: Poems for Men,* by Robert Bly, James Hillman, and Michael Meade (1992). The men's website www.menweb.org offers this comprehensive review of the former: "Moramarco and Zolynas bring together a comprehensive and widely representative selection of poetry reflecting both the diversity and the commonality of male experience in the United States today. The poems collected in Men of Our Time--257 from more than 170 poets--include a wide mix of ethnic and racial perspectives that reflect the multicultural tenor of American life. They reveal men's most intimate feelings about the loss of childhood, sexual anxieties and fantasies, aging, self-sufficiency and dependency, and the perennial quest for a masculine identity. Above all, the poems are unapologetically grounded in a distinctly male experience or imagination. This book reclaims a poetry that is connected to and expressive of men's lives in the closing decade of the twentieth century."

Men of Our Time includes poems by: Robert Bly, Raymond Carver, James Dickey, Allen Ginsberg, Donald Hall, Michael S. Harper, Robert Hass, Robert Hayden, Steve Kowit, Clarence Major, James Merrill, W. S. Merwin, Simon Ortiz, Robert Pinsky, Ishmael Reed, Jerome Rothenberg, Charles Simic, Gary Soto, Gary Snyder, and Richard Wilbur.

Sections of this anthology include:

- Boys Becoming Men
- Sons Seeing Fathers
- Sons and Their Mothers
- Fathers and Their Sons
- Fathers and Their Daughters
- Men and Women
- Brothers, Friends, Lovers and Others
- Men at War
- The Hearts of Men

The second anthology is *Rag and Bone Shop of the Heart: Poems for Men,* by Robert Bly, James Hillman and Michael Meade (1992). The following unattributed review was listed on the website www.menstuff.org. "How does the work of men connect to poetry? To this day in Kazakhstan roomfuls of men sit listening to a poet chant long narratives. We recall the importance of poetry in the lives of Norse farmers, Icelandic shepherds, Greek olive growers and fishermen. Their attention cannot be explained in terms of literacy or electricity - that they can't read or watch television. Rather, the question becomes how do the life of men and the life of a culture connect to poetry? While our European-American tradition questions and argues, and has to teach poetry to sullen students in English classes, other cultures, speaking Spanish, Russian, Arabic, to say nothing of the many tongues of Africa and the Indian subcontinent, grow up inside poems, drenched through with poetic metaphors and rhythms. As we learn to criticize, to take a poem apart, to get its meaning, they learn to listen and to recite. We live in a poetically underdeveloped nation. Blake, Yeats, James Wright, Anna Akhmatova, David Ignatow, D. H. Lawrence, William Carlos Williams, Etheridge Knight, Sharon Olds, Theodore Roethke, Marianne Moore, Cesar Vallejo - much great poetry was been written in the last century. A poem read silently or aloud from this book can't help but move you."

Encouraging men to create their own poems can be powerful work. The depths to which a man will mine the gems of his emotional self, *when* given permission, are immeasurable. In his book *Writing from the Body,* John Lee (1994) details how a man might begin the process of awakening his writer's soul and quieting his inner critic. He offers many powerful exercises designed to help break through our mental, physical, and emotional barriers to writing.

Poetry can often help a man cut through his intellect and tap into a hidden part of himself that none have ever seen. The following is a poem that was written by Chris from Chapter Two, who sought help with his rage:

Healing

I cannot remember the first time I felt the power of aggression.
The swelling of the chest, the pounding of the heart
I remember being afraid of myself

Afraid of the pain
Not wanting to inflict pain
Unable to bear the pain in my head, in my heart, in my soul
Lashing out because I couldn't lash in

violence
There was a time when I was paralyzed
I couldn't be violent if I tried
I had seen the damage
I had felt the fear of the flying fist

I was punched into it
Kicked over it
Knocked out of it
Heart heaving, heavily breathing
Blood streaming, pain searing

Thirty years have past
Now I'm caught in the cog of my own dysfunction
Alone because of my fear
Too intelligent to ask for help
Too important to be revealed

I am sorry
I beg forgiveness
I scream for healing
I plead for life…..

Chris's poem gives the reader a glimpse into the soul of a man seeking redemption.

Encouraging men to write poems to a particular person or addressing a particular issue can have profound results. A man wrote the following poem to his daughter:

Men's Group
at first I said,
"I have a doctor's appointment."
not wanting to admit therapy to my daughter
then she asked, "Is it just a check-up
or is something wrong?"
caught in the confused innocence of the lie
I said, "Actually I'm just going to talk,
There are doctors there,
a lawyer, and other good men."
Then with the piercing opacity of an eleven year old
she asked, "Do you talk about the cost of health care?"
stumbling through the lost honesty of a father
I said, "No, not really, but sometimes if you have a problem
it is easier to work it out talking with other people."
"What do you talk about?" she asked
I wanted to tell her about shame,
about the relentless unbearable weight of depression
about the forever open wounds of abuse,
how hard it is at times to separate the boy from the man,
about parents we all wanted but never had.
But I couldn't and I didn't
tell her all this

for some things are never clear
until you stray, step in it, and take the time
to scrape it from your sole.

The following poem might leave the reader pondering the values that our children inherit from us. It was written by John Dyben, spiritual counselor and friend of the authors.

the beard
d. john dyben

speak to me says the child as she pulls upon the beard
of her father who puts down his coffee to see her
curious and captured in the world of safety called daddy's lap
and he smiles a tired smile
looking at the face of years gone by and many years to come

and with a slight tilt to her head she asks
why the people stand at the red lights and hold up signs
and hold out their hands
and always look so very sad
so very tired and old and sad

and why when she went to the zoo did the goats eat grass
and people can't do that
but they can eat broccoli and she doesn't like it

and he marvels at the little foolish wonders and sighs at the thought
that someday she will learn
not the answers to these questions for we know he thinks
they lie in a region far beyond the realm of our wisdom
and so we will teach her and she will learn

she will learn to forget those questions with hiding answers
she will learn to forget the tired old man with
two shoes and not much more and she
will not have to reason why even they don't match

for who are we if we cannot enjoy
the top of this heap and who am i he thinks if i
cannot teach my little one to sit and watch and forget

and so says he with beard and coffee
years and wisdom
house and land
and so says he with wife and children
run and racing
wind and sand
you see my child this life will one day
be your own and capture you
and you will have no need to worry
about the old man's miss matched shoes

i see said the child with lips of purity as she released his beard

The last use of poetry that will be discussed here is Group Poetry. An interesting phenomenon occurs when a group of men offer what appear to be disconnected thoughts, without knowing the purpose. The following string of lines is the result of eight men, after completing a guided breath meditation with the directive to write down their vision, speaking aloud whatever sentence had come up for them to help them on their journey.

Responsibility over fear.
The world may be unpredictable, but stability will follow.
Trust the unknown adventure.
My feelings are the same, whether guiding or leading.
Life is good, self as others, others as self.

Uncertainty can be scary, or exciting and fun.
Trust makes the difference.
Care, power, self-reliance, superiority, ego.
Let go, be at peace.

However you choose to use it, poetry can be a powerful tool.

CHAPTER TWENTY ONE
Activities

If we all did the things we are capable of doing, we would literally astound ourselves.
Thomas Edison

Adventure therapy is a type of experiential therapy that requires people to work together in groups or challenges an individual to overcome a challenge and go beyond their normal comfort level. Activity therapy of this nature addresses issues such as group and family dynamics, problem-solving skills, communication, leadership styles, and support. Programs such as Outward Bound, youth programs, correctional programs, and corporate team-building have used adventure and activity therapy for over forty years. ROPES (Reality-Oriented-Physical-Experience-Services) and Initiatives have been used in residential addiction treatment programs, getting to issues that traditional talk therapy cannot, or at least getting there more quickly. Family secrets, control issues, fear, self-awareness, memories of past traumas, communication patterns, and issues of faith and trust frequently surface in adventure therapy.

ROPES has also been used in corporations, with volunteers, and with church and youth groups to achieve a variety of goals:

- Discover internal resources in the group
- Discover new skills and reduce stress within the group
- Motivate and revitalize
- Discover and build spirituality

When the subject of a ROPES course is brought up in conversation, many people visualize an obstacle course filled with various tortuous and humiliating devices. For some people, the fear of the unknown is so great that they will go to any length to avoid experiencing a ROPES program. However, for those who take the risk and attend a ROPES day, their lives can be changed forever. The experience is a "challenge-by-choice" philosophy which lets the participants decide to what extent they wish to participate in each activity. Within the first twenty minutes the fear fades as most people realize that ROPES is a different and fun way to learn how to work as a team by working through personal blocks. Success is determined by the group and is based on finding value in people's efforts.

Experiential learning models vary, but generally there are four distinct phases that comprise the learning cycle:

1. Experience
2. Reflection
3. Processing
4. Application back to experience

ROPES create a shared experience that sets the stage for learning. This experience allows the participant to look back and examine what he saw, felt, and thought during the event. The intent is to help participants understand what happened at a cognitive, affective, and behavioral level before, during, and after the activity. It is during this stage that the participant examines patterns of thoughts, feelings, and behaviors that occurred and tries to make links with similar occurrences in his life. Meanwhile, a certified ROPES Facilitator can see and learn a great deal about the participants. Often, he will notice patterns of behavior and interactions of which neither the individuals nor their team are aware. As a result, the challenge becomes how to help participants become aware of their thoughts, feelings, and behavior and how to transfer this knowledge to their home, work, or school setting.

High ROPES courses and other fixed low element challenges can be expensive. There are portable challenge courses that cost far less than the construction of fixed platforms. Other low-cost activities are group jump rope, group juggling, minefield games, tug-of-war, hoop relay, rodeo throws, "traffic jam," and other games that involve little to no materials costs. By paying attention to props and simple things around the house and thinking creatively, one can discover ways to develop one's own adventure kit on a budget.

Activities are powerful complements to traditional group work. Clients' stories are often revealed more swiftly through activities. Clinicians need training in the use of activities as they can be very powerful tools and need to be utilized appropriately. Activities are not parlor games to be used cavalierly. Rather, they need to be used skillfully and under close supervision and training. The following examples are feedback from two male ROPES course participants:

"As the day went on I thought nothing of my past and only thought of the present, which made me realize that I can't dwell on bad times. This is an important lesson for me as I move on with my life. I was also able to see the faces of my peers as I grabbed for their hands for help. It's getting easier to ask for help from other men and to face my fears."

"Today we learned how to trust each other. I learned perseverance and determination to not give up on things in front of me. I learned that reaching up and pulling myself up was like asking God to help me up, giving me the strength and courage to fight for my life. Reaching down to help someone else up was like using what God gave me to help them on their path. I also learned that if you fall or fail it's a lot easier to get back up with the support and encouragement of others."

For further information on ROPES course work, how to build one, where to get certified, and where to find one in your area, simply type the keywords "ROPES Courses" into your web browsing search engine.

QUESTIONNAIRES

Questionnaires

As discussed throughout, men do well with concrete tasks, such as homework assignments and questionnaires. The following questionnaires can be used in various phases of treatment.

Being a Man

What have you learned about men?

1. How would you complete these sentences:

Men are…

Men usually…

Men never…

Boys are different than girls because they…

Boys lack…

Boys should be able to…

Boys won't want to…

Compared to girls, boys are more…

Compared to boys, girls are more…

Most of the men in my life have been…

2. Think of a time in your life when a man came through for you, supported you. Who was that person? What did he provide? What do you take from that experience?

3. What are some of your expectations of women? That they put their needs aside

in favor of men's, act less smart than men, hide their intelligence, look to men to care for financial or physical tasks, be dependent on men, acquiesce to men's demands, take care of children, cook, clean house, defer to male authority, manage the feelings in a family or relationship?

4. Which (if any) of these expectations were present in your family? What were you taught? What occurred in your family? Which of these expectations do you see your son or his friends adopting? Which do you find it hard to let go of as expectations for yourself?

5 How did you cope with the pressure to act like a man? When you were young did you feel you were tough enough? Did you try to act tougher? Were you disrespected by adults for not acting like a man? What names were you called? Were you hit by your parents? By anyone else? What do you carry from these experiences?

6. What cultural, racial, or religious traditions do you identify with? What traditions do you value? What parts have lacked meaning for you? What traditions would you like to pass on to your sons? How would you describe your spiritual life?

7. How would you describe your physical life? Do you feel tired, warm, do you get enough sleep, do you eat properly, exercise adequately?

8. What feelings of loss and grief do you have?

9. When you were a child, did your family use physical discipline? What was the effect on you? Were you verbally mistreated, put down, teased, told you were stupid, or subjected to other negative comments? What were the effects of verbal abuse?

10.What do you value about sports? What do you consider questionable about sports? What sports did you participate in as a youth? Now? What sports do you watch now? How important is it for you to win? What would you like to pass on to boys about sports?

11. What messages were you given about women's bodies? Comments made about their bodies? How did you learn about sexuality? From whom? What were you told about men's bodies?

Turning Points in Your Life

Write your earliest memories of:

1. Your first day of school, first love, first kiss
2. Most recent illness
3. Your school years, especially high school
4. First job, first significant achievement, first sense of failure
5. Career changes
6. Marriage(s), children, births, weddings, life changes
7. First and most recent experience with death

Key Questions

1. Where do you want to be in five years, living, working?
2. Describe the qualities of your relationships.
3. What activities give you meaning? Painful memories, experiences?
4. If someone were to give you a testimonial dinner, what would you want said about you?
5. How would you describe your purpose in living? Your place in the universe?
6. What gift would you give to your family today if all things were possible to give?

You and Your Father

1. Describe your father; what do you remember about him? What kind of person is/was he? What did he talk with you about? What didn't he talk about? How did he express his feelings? What feelings did he express? How did he relate to women, children, other men?
2. Complete this sentence: "What my father passed on to me was...."
3. If your father was standing in front of you today, how would you complete this sentence: "Dad, I needed you to...."
4. For what have you blamed your father? Your mother?

5. What other "father figures" were in your life growing up? Who were your heroes? What did you learn from them?

6. What qualities do you think are important in a father?

Work and Overwork

Check all that apply:

- ☐ My family complains about my absence at evening meals because I am working late.
- ☐ I bring work home often.
- ☐ I have uncomfortable feelings about my strong work focus.
- ☐ At work I experience frustration about not seeming to ever get caught up.
- ☐ I often feel best when I am very busy, whether at work or home.
- ☐ I call into work at least twice while on vacation.
- ☐ I postponed or changed my vacation dates at least once during the past five years.
- ☐ I have been quietly harboring a desire to work less and get off the work treadmill.
- ☐ I feel angry about all that my employer expects of me.
- ☐ Those close to me often express displeasure about my being away so much on business trips.
- ☐ I feel guilty when I leave work on time.

Answer the following questions.

1. What bothers me most about my current job and/or work climate?

2. If I imagine myself at the age of 65 reflecting on my life, what would have been important to me and what would not?

3. Have I shared my dissatisfaction about my current job situation with those I care about? If not, why not?

4. If I had more personal time available, what is one way I would spend it?

5. Can I downshift at work? What is stopping me from doing so?

6. What is most important in my life right now? What is my greatest concern or fear about work?

7. If I created space for myself with work, what would I do instead?

8. On average, how much time per week would I like to carve away from my work?

Men and Money

1. Describe your current attitude about money. How important is it to you? Do you derive security from it? Do you use it to measure your self-worth? To measure your success? What does money mean to you?

2. Do you have a sense that you have enough money, assets? If not, how much more do you think you need to feel comfortable? To feel secure?

3. What would it mean to you to lose your assets? Your life savings? What would it mean to be more poor than you are?

4. What is your current practice with money, saving, spending, hoarding, self-indulgence?

5. Do you believe your current attitude and practice with respect to money enhance or detract from your spiritual life, your recovery?

6. How do you think you need to change your current attitude and practice with respect to money?

7. List your material possessions: cars, houses, stereos, computers, clothing, leisure sporting equipment?

8. How do you feel about these assets and possessions? How important are they to you? What would it be like if you lost them? What would you least like to lose?

Men and Sex

1. Describe your current sex life. How do you feel about your sex life?

2. On a scale of 1-10, 1 being the worst sex life on the world and 10 the best ever, how would you rate your current sex life? Why? Your past sex life? Why?

3. What is your current attitude about sexuality?

4. In what way do you believe your current sexual practices help/hurt your emotional, physical, and spiritual well-being?

5. In what ways, if any, do you think you need to change your attitudes and practices about sex?

You and your Partner(s)

1. Give a brief history of your personal, intimate relationships. Describe issues and concerns in these relationships.

2. What patterns have you noticed in your relationships? Were your relationships of short or long duration? Intense? Passionless? Passionate? Were you happy? What would you do differently now?

3. Do men around you avoid intimacy? How could you be more intimate? With whom? What ways do you use to avoid intimacy?

4. What would you gain by being closer to other men in your life?

5. List three things you like to tell another man. Are there things you don't know how to say, things about which you're embarrassed, ashamed?

6. Do you find it embarrassing to talk with men about personal information? What specifically do you find embarrassing to talk about with other men?

7. Write the name of one man you'd like to be closer to. How can you make that happen?

8. Write the name of one man you love, one you have loved, one you care about, one who cares for you.

Men and their Children

1. What kind of boys do you want to raise?
   - To be connected to the environment?
   - To express a variety of feelings?
   - To take care of themselves physically and emotionally so they do not expect others to take care of them?
   - To understand the social, political, and economic systems they live and work in?
   - To treat men and women as equals?
   - To treat others with respect, fairness??
   - To help others: the sick, poor, needy

2. What kind of world do you want to create?

3. What do men stand for?

4. How different are boys and girls?

5. Make a list of what you consider to be male and female qualities.

6. Is there an age beyond which you find it hard to hug or hold boys? Why?

7. How do you withhold affection from older boys? Men?

8. Describe a time when you worried your son or another boy wasn't tough enough.

9. How do you encourage boys to toughen up, suck up the pain, act like a man?

10. What kind of men do we need today?

11. Who are your "sons"? Boys to whom you act like a parent?

12. Which boys are hardest to see as your "sons"? Suburban, urban, rural, poor, well-off, disabled, gay, bisexual, African American, Asian, Latino, Jewish, Native American, White, immigrant, gang members?

13. Are you uncomfortable when your son comes home defeated, scared, having run from a fight? When he cries? Are you fully present to him then, or do you panic, withdraw from him?

14. Do you talk to your sons about personal matters? Do you listen to them?

15. In what ways have you assumed your sons or other boys you interact with are heterosexual? How would you respond if they were gay, bisexual?

16. When you were growing up, what were the messages given you about homosexuality? How old were you then? Where do you notice homophobia in the boys around you?

17. Appreciating boys: What do you love about your sons? What is unique about them? Positive qualities? Challenges they face?

18. Are there situations when you think it is OK to hit a child? To punish a child? To threaten a child? What do you gain/lose from threats, from hitting a child?

You and Children

1. To whom are you a father figure (biologically, socially, psychologically)?

2. Who are other youth to whom you might be a father figure?

3. If you have daughters, how can you support them? Sons?

4. How can you teach your sons to respect women, to treat women as equals?

5. What are ways you can teach children to be proud of their race, culture, religion, heritage, and to know about and respect the heritages of others?

6. How can you be a good model of tolerance and respect for youth?

7. What was the last time you told others/children you loved them?

Helping Children

Answer yes or no to the following questions:

1. Do I love, acknowledge, and respect the young in my life?
2. Do I tell them at least once a day that I love them?
3. Do I avoid blaming them for their mistakes?
4. Do I take my anger, frustrations, past hurts, and disappointments out on them?
5. Do I challenge them inappropriately? Do I talk straightforwardly to them?
6. Do I help them heal their hurts?
7. Do I share power with them in an appropriate manner?
8. Do I help them work together and support each other?

A Graph of Your Losses

Draw a timeline of your life. Include all the significant losses you have experienced. Date the losses. Write a sentence about what impact these losses have had on your life. What beliefs have you gained from each of these losses, either beliefs that constitute wisdom, or negative beliefs about your life?

One Year to Live Exercise

Here's the bad news: you have been given one year to live.

Here's the good news: you have unlimited resources to do whatever you wish to do.

Question: What would you do?

Write a personal creed, what you personally believe in.

Conclusion

And now to end this Manual on a note of humor (hopefully!):

Why Men are Happier than Women

- People never stare at your chest when talking to you
- You know stuff about tanks
- A 5-day trip requires 1 suitcase
- Your underwear is $8 a 3-pack
- You don't see wrinkles in clothes
- The same hairstyle lasts for decades
- You only have to shave your face and neck
- You do Christmas shopping for 25 people in 25 minutes on Dec. 24th
- Your last name stays put
- Car mechanics tell you the truth
- You can wear a T-shirt to a water park
- You can wear no T-shirt to a water park
- The world is a urinal
- Wedding dress, $3000; tux rental, $80
- One mood all day
- Phone calls last 30 seconds
- Wrinkles add character

BIBLIOGRAPHY

Ackerman, R. *Silent Sons: A Book For and About Men.* New York: Fireside, 1993.

Addis, M.E., and Mahalik, J.R. "Men, Masculinity, and the Contexts of Help Seeking." In *American Psychologist,* Volume 58, Number 1, January 2001, 5-14.

Alderfer, Charlene. "The Effects of Gender on the Supervisory Process," Unpublished Doctoral Dissertation, University of Massachusetts, MA, 1991.

Bandura, A. *Principles of Behavior Modification.* New York: Holt, Rinehart & Winston, 1969.

Brannon, R., and Juni, S., A scale for measuring attitudes about masculinity. Psychological Documents *14(1), 6. (MS No 2617), 1984.*

Beitman, B., *The Structure of Individual Psychotherapy.* New York: Guilford Press, 1987.

Bell C.C., Thompson J.P., Lewis D, et al: Misdiagnosis of alcohol-related organic brain syndromes: implications for treatment, in *Treatment of Black Alcoholics.* Edited by Brisbane FL, Womble M. Binghamton, NY: Haworth, 1985.

Blazina, C., and Watkins, C.E. Masculine gender role conflict: Effects on college men's psychological well-being, chemical substance usage, and attitudes toward help-seeking. *Journal of Counseling Psychology,* 51, 461-465, 1996.

Bly, R., Hillman, J., and Meade, M. *Rag and Bone Shop of the Heart: Poems for Men.* New York, NY: HarperCollins, 1992.

Brady, K.T., and Randall, C.L. Gender differences in substance use disorders. *Psychiatric Clinics of North America* 22(2):241-252, 1999.

Brehm, S. *Intimate Relationships.* New York: Random House, 1985.

Brooks, G.R. Masculinity and men's mental health. *Journal of American College Health* 49(6):285-297, 2001.

Budman, S. *Theory and Practice of Brief Therapy.* New York: Guilford Press, 1988.

Capacchione, L. *Recovery of Your Inner Child.* Fireside, New York: Simon and Schuster, 1991.

Carnes, P. *Out of the Shadows: Understanding Sexual Addiction.* MN: Hazelden, 1992.

Center for Disease Control (2006) www.cdc.gov/ncipc/dvp/suicide/ (Accessed December 7, 2006).

Center for Substance Abuse Treatment. *Substance Abuse Treatment and Men.* Treatment Improvement Protocol (TIP) Series. Rockville, MD: Substance Abuse and Mental Health Services Administration, in development i.

Center for Substance Abuse Treatment. *A Guide to Substance Abuse Services for Primary Care Clinicians.* Treatment Improvement Protocol (TIP) Series 24. Rockville, MD: Substance Abuse and Mental Health Services Administration, DHHS Publication No. (SMA) 97-3139, 1997.

Cook, D. *Internalized shame scale.* Menomonie, WI: University of Wisconsin-Stout, 1989.

Cochran, S., and Rabinowitz, F. *Men and Depression: Clinical and Empirical Perspectives.* San Diego: Academic Press, 2000.

David, D. & Brannon, R. *The Male Sex Role: Our Culture's Blueprint of Manhood, and What It's Done for Us Lately.* MA: Addison-Wesley Publishing Company, 1976.

Dennis, L.K., and Hayes, R.B. Alcohol and prostate cancer. *Epidemiologic Reviews* 23(1):110-114, 2001.

Edelwich, J., and Brodsky, A. *Sexual Dilemmas for the Helping Professional* (rev. ed.). New York: Brunner/Mazel, 1991.

Efthim, P. W., Kenny, M. E., & Mahalik, J. R. Gender role stress in relation to shame, guilt and externalization. *Journal of Counseling and Development,* 79, 430-438. 2001.

Eisler, R. M. The relationship between masculine gender role stress and men's health risk: The validation of a construct. In R. F. Levant & W. S. Pollack (Eds.), A new psychology of men (pp. 207-225). New York: Basic Books, 1995.

Emanuele, M.A., and Emanuele, N. Alcohol and the male reproductive system. *Alcohol Research and Health* 25(4):282-287. 2001.

Emanuele, M.A., and Emanuele, N.V. Alcohol's effects on male reproduction. *Alcohol Health and Research World* 22(3):195-201,1998.

Epstein, R.S. *Keeping Boundaries: Maintaining Safety and Integrity in the Psychotherapeutic Process.* Washington, DC: American Psychiatric Press, 1994.

Farrell, W. *Why Men Are the Way they Are.* Columbus, OH: McGraw-Hill, 1986.

Garfinkel, L., McLanahan, S.S., Meyer, D.R., and Seltzer, J.A., eds. *Fathers Under Fire: The Revolution in Child Support Enforcement.* New York: Russel Sage

Foundation, 1998.

Gilligan, C. *In a Different Voice,* (2nd edition) Cambridge, MA: Harvard University Press, 1992.

Goldberg, H. *The Hazards of Being Male: Surviving the Myth of Masculine Privilege.* Plainview, NY: Nash Publishing, 1976.

Greenberg, S. *Right from the Start: A Guide to Nonsexist Child-Rearing.* Boston: Houghton Mifflin, 1979.

Gurian, M. *What Stories Does My Son Need?* New York: Tarcher/Putnam, 2000.

Gutheil, T.G., and Brodsky, A. *Preventing Boundary Violations in Clinical Practice.* New York: Guilford Press, 2008.

Halpern, D. F. The disappearance of cognitive gender differences: what you see depends on where you look. *American Psychologist,* 44, 1156-1158, 1989.

Haley, J. *Uncommon Therapy: The Psychiatric Techniques of Milton H Erickson.* New York: Basic, 1973.

Hanson, G.R., In drug abuse, gender matters. *NIDA NOTES* 17(2):3-4, 2002.

Heath, A.C. Genetic influences on alcoholism risk: A review of twin and adoption studies. *Alcohol Health and Research World* 19(3):166-171, 1995.

Hesley, J.W. & Hesley, J.G. *Rent two films and let's talk in the morning: Using popular movies in psychotherapy.* NY: John Wiley & Sons, 1998.

Hser, Y., & Anglin, M.D. Cost-effectiveness of drug treatment: Relevant issues and alternative longitudinal modeling approaches. In W. S. Cartwright & J. M. Kaple (eds.) NIDA monograph on *Economic Costs, Cost-Effectiveness, Financing, and Community-based Drug Treatment,* 1991.

Jang, K.L., Livesley, W.J., and Vernon, P.A. Gender-specific etiological differences in alcohol and drug problems: A behavioral genetic analysis. *Addiction* 92(10):1265-1276, 1997.

Johnson, K.W., Anderson, N.B., Bastida, E., Kramer, B.J., Williams, D. & Wong, M. Panel II: Macrosocial and environmental influences on minority health. *Health Psychology,* 14, 601-612., 1995.

Joshua, J., and DiMenna, D. *Read Two Books and Let's Talk Next Week.* IN: John Wiley, 2000.

Keen, S. *Fire in the Belly: On Being a Man.* New York: Bantam Books, 1991.

Kindlom, D., and Thompson, M. *Raising Cain: Protecting the Emotional Life of Boys.* New York: Ballentine Books, 1999.

Kipnis, A. *Angry Young Men.* Jossey-Boss Publishers, 1999.

Kivel, P. *Boys Will Be Men: Raising Our Sons for Courage, Care, and Community.* BC, Canada: New Society Publishers, 1999.

Kivel, P. *Men's Work: How to Stop the Violence that Tears Our Lives Apart.* MN: Hazelden, 1992.

Lee, J. *Facing the Fire: Experiencing and Expressing Anger Appropriately.* New York: Bantam Books, 1993.

Lee, J. *Writing from the Body: For Writers, Artists, and Dreamers Who Long to Free Their Voice.* New York: St Martin's Griffin, 1994.

Lee, J. *The Missing Peace: Solving the Anger Problem for Alcoholics, Addicts, and Those Who Love Them.* Deerfield Beach, FL: Health Communications Inc, 2006.

Lemle, R., and Mishkind, M.E. Alcohol and masculinity. *Journal of Substance Abuse Treatment* 6(40:213-222, 1989.

Levant, R., Hirsch, L., Celentano, E., Cozza, T., Hill, S., MacEachern, M., Marty, N., & Schnedeker, J. The male role: An investigation of contemporary norms. *Journal of Mental Health Counseling,* 14, 325-337, 1992.

Liebschutz , J., Savetsky, J.B., Saitz, R., Horton, N.J., Lloyd-Travaglini, C., and Samet, J.H. The relationship between sexual and physical abuse and substance abuse consequences. *Journal of Substance Abuse Treatment* 22(3):121-128, 2002.

Mathias, R. *The Addiction Severity Index.* NIDA Notes 9(2):8-9, 1994. www.treatment.org/Externals/Tip-14/tip-14apa.htm

Mee-Lee, D. *ASAM's placement criteria: What's new.* Behavioral Health Management Volume 25, No. 3. May/June 2005.

Mercer, D., and Woody, G. "Addiction Counseling." Unpublished manuscript, University of Pennsylvania/VAMC Center for Studies of Addiction, 1992.

Miller, W.R., & Hester, R.K. Treating the problem drinker: Modern approaches. In W. R. Miller (Ed.), *The addictive behaviors: Treatment of alcoholism, drug abuse, smoking and obesity* pp. 11-141). Oxford: Pergamon Press, 1980.

Miller, W., and Rollnick, S. *Motivational Interviewing: Preparing People for Change.* New York: Guilford Press, 2002.

Miller, W.R., Wilbourne, P.L., & Hettema, J.E. What works? A summary of alcohol treatment outcome research. In R. K. Hester & W. R. Miller (Eds.), Handbook of Alcoholism Treatment Approaches: Effective Alternatives (3nd ed., pp. 13-63). Boston, MA: Allyn and Bacon, 2003.

Moramarco, F., and Zolynas, A. editors, *Men of Our Time: An Anthology of Male Poetry in Contemporary America.* Athens, GA: University of Georgia Press, 1992.

National Alliance to End Homelessness, 2006. www.endhomelessness.org (Accessed February 5, 2005).

National Institute on Alcohol Abuse and Alcoholism. *Alcohol and AIDS.* Alcohol Alert No. 15, Bethesda, MD: National Institute on Alcohol Abuse and Alcoholism, 1992. http://www.niaaa.nih.gov/publications/aa15.htm [Accessed

June 3, 2003].

National Institute on Alcohol Abuse and Alcoholism. *Tenth Special Report to the U.S. Congress on Alcohol and Health.* Bethesda, M.D: National Institute on Alcohol Abuse and Alcoholism, 2000. http://www.niaaa.nih.gov/publications/10report/into.pdf [Accessed June 3, 2003].

National Institute on Drug Abuse **(NIDA)** Therapy Manuals www.drugabuse.gov/TXManuals/ (Accessed December 5, 2007).

O'Donahue, J., *Anam Cara: A Book of Celtic Wisdom.* New York: Harper Collins, 1998.

O'Neil, J. M. Gender role conflict and strain in men's lives: Implications for psychiatrists, psychologists, and other human service providers. In. Solomon, K &. Levy, N.B (Eds.), Men in transition: Changing male roles, theory, and therapy. New York: Plenum Publishing Co., 1982.

O'Neil, J.M., Good, G.E., & Holmes, S. Fifteen years of theory and research on men's gender role conflict: New paradigms for empirical research. In R. F. Levant and W. S. Pollock (Eds.), A new psychology of men. New York: Basic Books, 1995.

Ouimette, P.C., Kimerling, R., Shaw, J.,and Moos, R.H. Physical and sexual abuse among women and men with substance use disorders. Alcoholism Treatment Quarterly 18(3):7-17, 2000.

Pollack, W. *Real Boys: Rescuing Our Sons from the Myths of Boyhood.* New York: Random House, 1999.

Powell, D.J. *Playing Life's Second Half: A Man's Guide for Turning Success into Significance.* Oakland, CA: New Harbinger, 2003.

Powell D.J., with Brodsky A. *Clinical Supervision in Alcohol and Drug Abuse Counseling: Principles, Models, Methods* (Revised Edition). San Francisco, CA: Jossey-Bass, 2004.

Rabinowitz, J., and Marjefsky, S., Predictors of being expelled from and dropping out of alcohol treatment. *Psychiatric Services* 49(2):187-189, 1998.

Real, T. *I Don't Want to Talk About It.* New York: Scribner, 1997.

Reamer, F.G. *Tangled Relationships: Managing Boundary Issues in the Human Services.* New York: Columbia University Press, 2001.

Rohr, R. *The Wild Man's Journey: Reflections on Male Spirituality.* New York: St. Anthony's Messenger Press, 1996.

Rosener, J. "How Women Lead," *Harvard Business Review,* Nov-Dec. 1990.

Rosenthal, H. *Favorite Counseling and Therapy Homework Assignments: Leading Therapists Share Their Most Creative Strategies.* Psychology Press, 2001.

Rosenthal, H. *Homework Makes a Good Counseling Session Even Better.* Counselor Magazine, July 2002.

SAMHSA (1996). www.oas.samhsa.gov (Accessed February 5, 2005).

Schneider, B. *The Cocaine Sex Connection: Understanding Our Sexual Acting Out.* MN: Hazelden, 1992.

Schneider J., and Weiss J. *Cybersex Exposed: Simple Fantasy or Obsession?.* Hazelden Information Education, 2001.

Schuckit, M.A., Daeppen, J.B., Tipp, J.E., Hesselbrock, M., and Bucholz, K.K. The clinical course of alcohol-related problems in alcohol dependent and non-alcohol dependent drinking women and men. *Journal of Studies on Alcohol* 59(5):581-590, 1998.

Shaffer, D., Gould, M.S., Fisher, P., Trautmann, P., Moeau, D., Kleinman, M., and Flory, M. (1999). Psychiatric diagnosis in child and adolescent suicide. *Archives of General Psychiatry,* 53, 339-348,1999.

Sheehy, G. *Understanding Men's Passages: Discovering the New Map of Men's Lives.* New York: Ballantine Books, 1998.

Solomon, G., *Reel Therapy.* New York: Lebhar-Friedman, 2001.

Swartz, J.A., and Lurigio, A.J. Psychiatric illness and comorbidity among adult male jail detainees in drug treatment. *Psychiatric Services* 50(12):1628-1630, 1999.

Tannen, D. *You Just Don't Understand: Women and Men in Conversation.* New York: William Morrow, 1990.

Thompson, E.H., & Pleck, J.H. The structure of male role norms. American Behavioral Scientist, 29, 531-543, 1986.

Tompkins, M.A. *Using Homework in Psychotherapy: Strategies, Guidelines, and Forms.* New York: The Guilford Press, 2004.

Tu, G.C., and Israel, Y. Alcohol consumption by Orientals in North America is predicted largely by a single gene. *Behavior Genetics* 25(1):59-65,1995.

US Dept. of Justice, (2004). www.ojp.usdoj.gov/bjs. (Accessed February 5, 2005).

Van Etten, M.L., and Anthony, J.C. Male-female differences in transitions from first drug opportunity to first use: Searching for subgroup variation by age, race, region, and urban status. *Journal of Women's Health & Gender-Based Medicine* 10(8):797-804, 2001.

Walters, G.D. The heritability of alcohol abuse and dependence: A meta-analysis of behavior genetic research. *American Journal of Drug and Alcohol Abuse* 28(3): 557-584, 2002.

Washton, A.M., and Stone-Washton, N. Abstinence and relapse in outpatient cocaine addicts. *Journal of Psychoactive Drugs,* 22(2):135-147, 1990.

Webber, G. "Feminist Models of Supervision," AAMFT Annual Conference, 1991.

Wegscheider-Cruse, S., and Cruse, J. *Understanding Co-Dependency.* Deerfield Beach, FL: Health Communications Inc, 1990.

Whyte, D. *The Heart Aroused: Poetry and the Preservation of the Soul in Corporate America.* New York: Currency Doubleday, 2002.

Williams, R., and Ricciardelli, L. Gender congruence in confirmatory and compensatory drinking, *The Journal of Psychology,* 133 (3), pp. 323-331, Heldref Publications, Washington, DC, 1999.

Wilsnack , R.W., Vogeltanz, N.D., Wisnack, S.C., and Harris, T.R. Gender differences in alcohol consumption and adverse drinking consequences: Cross-cultural patterns. *Addiction* 95(2):251-265, 2000.

Worthman, C. "Biocultural Interactions in Human Development," in *Juvenile Primates Life History, Development, and Behavior.* New York: Oxford University Press, 1993.

Yalom, I.D., *The Theory and Practice of Group Psychotherapy.* New York: Basic Books, 1970.